हठयोगप्रदीपिका

hatha yoga pradipika

SIVANANDA YOGA VEDANTA CENTRE
51 Felsham Road
London SW15 1AZ
Tel: 0181-780 0160
Fax: 0181-780 0128
Email:siva@dial.pipex.com
Yoga Classes, Books and Tapes

हठयोगप्रदीपिका
hatha yoga pradipika

**The Classic Guide for the Advanced Practice of Hatha Yoga
(Kundalini Yoga)**

**As Written Down in the Seventeenth Century from Ancient
Sources by Yogi Swatmarama**

Reprinted from the 1893 Edition

Containing the Commentary Jyotsna of Brahmananda

**Here Containing for the First Time
The Practical Commentary of Swami Vishnu-devananda**

*World famed authority on Hatha and Raja Yoga
Founder of International Sivananda Yoga Vedanta Centers*

OM LOTUS PUBLICATIONS

First Printing 1987
Second Printing 1992
Third Printing 1997

**Copyright © 1987
by the International Sivananda Yoga Vedanta Centers**

No part of this book may be reproduced without written permission from the
author with the exception of brief passages quoted in review.

ISBN: 0-931546/02/8

Printed in India
for
**OM Lotus Publishing Company
243 West 24th Street
New York, NY 10011, USA**
email: OmLotus@sivananda.org

owned and operated by Sivananda Yoga Vedanta Centers
Sivananda Ashram Yoga Camp – Headquarters
8th Avenue, Val Morin, Quebec JOT 2RO CANADA
Tel: (819) 322-3226
Fax: (819) 322-5876
email: HQ@sivananda.org

TABLE OF CONTENTS

Swami Vishnu-devananda (1927-1993)

To commemorate the 70th anniversary of the birth

of Swami Vishnu-devananda

PREFACE TO THIRD EDITION

OM NAMO NARAYANAYA

December, 1997

Four years have passed since Swami Vishnu-devananda left his physical body. As his close students and staff watched, Swamiji achieved that state of Samadhi which he so yearned for, and spoke of so beautifully in his commentaries on the *Hatha Yoga Pradipika*.

Often, at the end of a Yoga Teachers' Training Course, Swamiji would extol the new graduates to be "teachers and not preachers." He meant that Yoga is an art and science to be practiced and learned first hand. Swamiji himself used his own body and mind as a laboratory. Whatever he read or heard, he experienced himself and could report first hand results.

Although True Knowledge cannot be learned from a book, scriptures such as the present one, are meant as guides. Together with an experienced teacher, they can steer the sincere student along the proper path.

In an effort to enhance the usefulness of the present edition, pictures, the original Sanskrit text, glossary and index have been included. It is offered with a prayer:

"May the whole world find Peace and Happiness."

Yours in His Service,
the staff and students of
The International Sivananda Yoga Vedanta Center

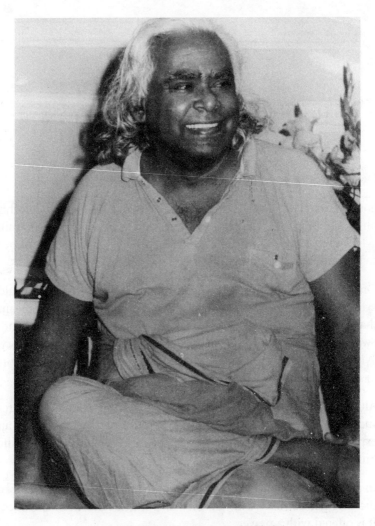

Published in honour of the 60th Birthday
"Diamond Jubilee Celebration"
of Swami Vishnu-devananda
by his disciples and devotees

PREFACE TO FIRST EDITION

I would like to begin by speaking about the spiritual path we are climbing through Yoga. You might say that it is an uphill climb. There are ups and downs. We climb up and then once again go down. There is no straight path to the top and there are many obstacles. In some places the road is wide but then suddenly it narrows. We come to a bush through which it is very difficult to penetrate, and even though we continue, we do not know where we are going.

So it is with the spiritual journey. In the beginning it is all very wonderful: "Ah, yes, I can do asanas, pranayama, etc.", but then suddenly you come to that big bush in your path and you don't know in which direction to go. If somehow you come out of the bush, you come next to a swamp. Some students disappear in the quicksand and never come out. Perhaps they see a beautiful girl or a handsome man and get married, and oh, they want to enjoy their life with children, home and family – once again swallowed by Maya, their spiritual purpose completely forgotten.

Nevertheless, it is possible to penetrate these obstacles and reach the top. Now you can see all around beautifully. Now you can meditate and enjoy full freedom. No more birth, no more death; you've got an eternal holiday.

These experiences are familiar to the yogi. He finds no smooth road to the top. Those who succeed come from different directions, having followed different teachers, but once they reach the top, everything is the same. On the way the obstacles will differ, but at the top the view is the same.

The purpose of the practice of Yoga is to give your life a boost, to put your spiritual progress in first gear. Then you may go into second gear and maybe into third gear where you can cruise comfortably after climbing the hills. This is unlike most worldly people who just coast downhill without knowing about brakes, thinking that happiness is somewhere down there, waiting. They go straight downhill, faster and faster into numerous disasters such as cancer, AIDS, high blood pressure, heart trouble. Soon it is too late and they crash. So even though it may seem very easy, please don't coast downhill. We will show you another way.

The path was laid out by the *Hatha Yoga Pradipika*, an ancient text used by Yogis to create the power to go uphill all the way to the top. This path was laid out by great beings called siddhas: Matsyendranath, his disciple Gorakshanath and others, fourteen in all. This is one of the earliest treatises on Hatha Yoga; all the modern books are based on it. It is the central route. All of us have only expanded and expounded on it in different ways.

In addition to following the practices laid out in the Hatha Yoga Pradipika, I strongly recommend the study of books such as Shankaracharya's *Viveka Chudamani,* and the *Srimad Bhagavatam.* The *Viveka Chudamani* is a very beautiful book, and those who follow its instruction will create the necessary dispassion to surmount the obstacles created by rajas (passion or activity). In addition, we also need devotion, because without God's grace we cannot reach the Source no matter how hard we strive. To help create this devotion, we read from the Bhagavatam.

This practice is not something I invented; it is the traditional method which I myself followed intensively when I was with Master Sivananda in the Himalayas. I lived in the forest where there were cobras and tigers. Sometimes I could hear the tigers from my cottage when they would come by to drink water and they would roar. I had only a flimsy door which they could easily have pushed through. Nevertheless, in such an environment I went through this training morning, noon, evening and midnight, practicing for almost fourteen hours daily. I hardly slept – just two or three hours a night. But I can't begin to describe the power that builds up.

Our purpose here is to increase the vibratory level in a very short time. In Sanskrit this work is expressed as "Shakti Sanchar." Shakti is the "power" and Sanchar means "awakening of." We want to make the Shakti move from its dormant or static state to the dynamic state through sadhana or spiritual practice. However, please be careful not to go beyond your capacity. Do not do too much at once, do not go too deep or too fast, do not work too intensively, or else a kickback will come. That is why I modify the practice to suit the particular evolution of my students. I never give a practice unless I myself have experienced it. Also, though I like discipline, I believe that this discipline must come from within. I show my students how this can be accomplished and then leave them to practice as if they were alone in the forest. To this is added just a little group practice for reinforcement. In addition, my students make out a resolve form and keep a spiritual diary which I look at to check their progress so that I can prescribe a little more or a little less of a particular practice. We meet together for an hour each day to talk about our practice, to receive some instruction about technical things and to improve the performance of some of these procedures.

My main instruction is to control the mind. Secondly, avoid unnecessary desires with one exception – desire to increase your will power. If you satisfy one desire, ten more will come to take its place, and then when will you ever be finished with all those desires? But if you develop your will power and kill even one desire, then you will be strong. Then you will easily kill ten more, and then a hundred.

Om Namah Sivaya!

Swami Vishnudevananda

EDITOR'S NOTE

We have used a text of the Hatha Yoga Pradipika which was printed in Adyar, India in 1893. It is a rare and especially faithful translation, much valued for the insightful commentary of Brahmananda (which is included as well). Although this edition was published more than one hundred years ago, the present editor has had to alter very little in order to make the text conform to modern usage. Insertions by the editor are printed in [brackets].

The text of the Pradipika is set in 12pt Officiana Italic.

The text of Brahmananda's commentary is set in 11pt Minion Italic and is indented.

The text in 11pt Minion (regular) type, is the commentary of Swami Vishnu-devananda, as given in a series of lectures at the first of the annual Sadhana Intensives held at the Sivananda Ashram Yoga Camp in Val Morin, Quebec, Canada in June, 1986.

This book is intended as an aid for those who wish to learn the advance practices of Hatha (Kundalini) Yoga from a qualified teacher. It is suggested that it also be used in conjunction with the *Complete Illustrated Book of Yoga* by Swami Vishnu-devananda, the *Sivananda Companion to Yoga* (known as the *Book of Yoga* in Britain), and *Yoga Mind & Body*.

Many of the instructions given here have been purposely veiled by the original writers, others need elaboration, and many require the guidance of a teacher for correction. Swami Vishnu-devananda has repeatedly stressed that these practices are not for beginners, and that to violate this caution is to put the psyche at risk. Please therefore, follow these instructions along with the guidance of your guru.

A Glossary has been prepared for this book for this third edition, in the hopes that this will be used as a reference manual for serious Yoga students on all levels.

हठयोगप्रदीपिका

hatha yoga pradipika

CHAPTER ONE

श्री आदिनाथाय नमोऽस्तु तस्मै योनोपदिष्टा हठयोगविद्या।
विभ्राजते   प्रोन्नतराजयोगमारोढुमिच्छोरधिरोहिणीव॥ १ ॥

(1) *I salute the primeval Lord, Siva, who taught to Parvati the Hatha Yoga Vidya, which is as a stairway for those who wish to attain the most excellent Raja Yoga.*

CHAPTER ONE

श्री आदिनाथाय नमोऽस्तु तस्मै योनोपदिष्टा हठयोगविद्या।
विभ्राजते   प्रोन्नतराजयोगमारोढुमिच्छोरधिरोहिणीव ॥ १ ॥

(1) I salute the primeval Lord, Siva, who taught to Parvati the Hatha Yoga Vidya, which is as a stairway for those who wish to attain the most excellent Raja Yoga.

Swatmarama begins the teaching in the traditional way, by prostrating before the gurus. First he prostrates before the Adi Guru, the first guru – Lord Siva, and then before his disciple Matsyendranath and his disciple Gorakshanath. Through their grace, Swatmarama expounds this great science.

Vidya means knowledge. The knowledge of Hatha Yoga was first taught by Siva to his consort Parvati, the Universal Mother.

The purpose of Hatha Yoga is to give you the knowledge of controlling these two energies "Ha" and "Tha" (Prana and Apana). Without this knowledge it is very difficult to gain that control over the mind, which is called Raja Yoga. Raja Yoga deals with the mind, Hatha Yoga works with the prana and apana. Many students make the mistake of considering Hatha Yoga to be mainly asanas, when actually asana is only one of the eight steps of Hatha Yoga. Furthermore, there is no real difference between Hatha Yoga and Raja Yoga. There is no possibility of attaining Raja Yoga without practice of Hatha Yoga, and vice versa. Hatha Yoga is the practical way to control the mind through control of the prana.

Look at the fluttering of the leaves on a tree. By watching this fluttering you can infer the speed of the wind, even though you cannot see the wind itself. In the same way, we cannot see the prana or the apana, or the motion of the mind or its thoughts. According to Raja Yoga, mind is like a lake, and thought the waves (or vrittis in Sanskrit). Raja Yoga is controlling and eventually stopping these waves of thought. In Sanskrit we say, "Yoga chitta vritti nirodha."

According to Patanjali, author of the [Raja] Yoga Sutras, there are five kinds of vrittis, some being positive and some not. Of these five, only one is entirely positive, and that is when the seer identifies with the Self (the Atman). This is only possible when the thought waves are slowed down. Then the seer sees, in the calm lake of the mind, his own Self (Atman). But, as long as the wind exists, we will see the tree moving, the leaves fluttering – sometimes quietly, sometimes violently, but always moving.

Hatha Yoga asks, "How do you stop these waves?" and "How does the seer see the Self?"

As the waves on the lake are created by the wind on the lake, so also the waves on the mind are created by the prana and apana. Sometimes this energy moves very fast, sometimes slow. And according to the nature of the prana/apana motion, the thought waves will be very intense or very slow. We call this rajasic or tamasic thought.

Tamasic waves are lethargic and sleepy, for then inertia prevails. It is not a still, peaceful state of mind, or an active state of mind; it is an inert state, where mind is incapable of doing anything. It just vegetates like a stone or a block of ice. Tamasic waves are very dull and gross, frozen like ice, so that you can't see your reflection even though the surface seems to be still. It is impossible to see what's at the bottom of the lake.

Rajasic waves are like a stormy sky. It is agitated. Waves arise on the lake, arise and dissolve continuously on the turbulent surface of the mind.

But in the sattvic state, the waves become still; there is no motion of the prana or apana because the energy has been diverted to the central channel, the Sushumna. Ordinarily, when these waves are projected, the prana/apana moves through the Ida and Pingala channels on the right and left sides of the body. This can be demonstrated by checking your brain waves.

Sometimes the right hemisphere is more active; sometimes it is the left that is more active. Waves from the left hemisphere are mostly analytical, mathematical, scientific, rational, etc. Generally, these are the waves most used by the Western mind. That is why you (in the West) have created beautiful cities and cars and complex technologies. It is because your left hemisphere most often dominates the right hemisphere. Even your religions emphasize the left, analytical side. When Christian monks go into seclusion, they indulge in contemplation rather than in meditation, and in Judaism, the usual rabbinical approach to religion is analytical.

Waves coming from the right brain are philosophical, devotional, compassionate, peaceful in nature, even though we use them mostly for inertia or for emotional things. Either you love or you hate somebody, and so you put the waves on a very gross or tamasic level.

The purpose of Yoga is to prevent either hemisphere from dominating the other, to create the sattvic state. That is why we meditate in a place where there is very little activity – just the simple natural motion of the trees in the breeze and occasionally the calls of some birds. In our ashrams we plant flowers. All this is to help calm the mind.

The main practice of Yoga is to control the left side of the brain by using the right brain. When the left brain is active, Ida is functioning and breath is moving through the right nostril. When the right brain is operating, the left nostril is opened and Pingala is functioning. Normally this changes every one and a half to two hours, alternating back and forth. But when the energy is not moving through either the left or right nadi, it must go through the Sushumna, and then the energy is balanced.

Moreover, the awareness of time and space is caused by this motion of waves of prana between the right and left channels. There is some similarity between samadhi and deep sleep. In deep sleep you are not aware of time or space because the vrittis are suppressed; they are not stopped as in samadhi. You might say that in deep sleep the vrittis are on ice – in cold storage. They will come back when the sun comes up to melt the ice. But in samadhi there are no vrittis at all. Ordinarily the only time we experience such quiet is during deep sleep, a state of inertia, but in samadhi the mental modifications have been suspended. Then there is balance between the right and left brains. For this we practice alternate nostril breathing because we can't directly affect the brain itself.

Brahmananda's Commentary: *Nearly every work on Yoga and the Tantras is in the form of an exposition by Siva, the great Yogi, to his wife, Parvati. The word "Hatha" is composed of the syllables "ha" and "tha," meaning the Sun and the Moon, i.e. Prana and Apana. Their yoga or union, i.e. pranayama, is called Hatha Yoga. In this stanza and throughout the work, it is stated that Hatha Yoga is only a means to Raja Yoga. "There can be no Raja Yoga without Hatha Yoga and vice versa."*

प्रणम्य श्रीगुरुं नाथं स्वात्मारामेण योगिना।
केवलं राजयोगाय हठविद्योपदिश्यते॥ २ ॥

(2) Swatmarama Yogi, having saluted his own guru, gives out the Hatha Vidya solely for the attainment of Raja Yoga.

Following tradition, he first salutes his own guru in order to get the benefit of the teaching. You must salute your teacher because God is manifesting the teaching through him. Here it is Siva who is manifesting through Swatmarama's teacher.

Raja Yoga means control of thought waves, something which is not possible without Hatha Yoga. Swatmarama is not talking about asanas or even about the physical breathing, but about the subtle current which creates the thought waves.

Brahmananda's Commentary: *By using the word "solely," he makes it plain that the object of practicing Hatha Yoga is to prepare oneself for Raja Yoga, and not to obtain the siddhis (psychic powers). These powers are only accidental and secondary. The course of Hatha Yoga is meant to give complete control over the bodily organs and the mind so that the yogi might keep good health and not be troubled during the ensuing course of Raja Yoga, which will lead him to Kaivalya or final emancipation.*

भ्रान्त्या बहुमतध्वान्ते राजयोगमजानताम्।
हठप्रदीपिकां धत्ते स्वात्माराम: कृपाकर:॥ ३ ॥

(3) To those who wander in the darkness of the conflicting sects, unable to obtain Raja Yoga, the merciful Swatmarama Yogi offers the light of Hatha Vidya.

You can translate the words "Raja Yoga" here to mean control of thought currents. Those who are unable to obtain Raja Yoga are those who are still unable to control their own thoughts when they meditate; their thoughts continue to come up. The aim of Raja Yoga is to stop the thought waves, but when you cannot do that, you try to learn to control the prana. In order to control the prana, you control the physical breath. In this way, through the physical you go to the subtle prana, and then to an even subtler level – to thought. As they are all interrelated, one affects the other.

What does he mean by "conflicting sects?" Someone will say to do this, another will say to repeat mantras or to do that. Hatha Yoga is a scientific approach to subduing the thought current by subduing the prana. That is accomplished when there are no waves. The seer sees Himself, the seer and the seen become one. The seer identifies with the Self. In this state there are no vrittis (thought waves). It is something like looking at the bright light of the sun or the high beam of an approaching car. After some time you are blinded. When the vrittis subside as a result of doing pranayama, that is called Raja Yoga. That state is the seer seeing the Self.

The "light of Hatha Vidya" is the knowledge of Hatha Yoga.

Brahmananda's Commentary: *Here the author says that it is impossible to obtain Raja Vidya by any other means than the Hatha Vidya. The name of the author, Swatmarama Yogi, is very suggestive. It means one who delights in communion with his higher Self. This represents the last of seven stages of knowledge (Jnana). The srutis [scriptures] say, "The*

*Brahmavarishta is one who sports and delights in his higher Self." The seven stages are thus described in the **Yoga Vasishta**, one of the most authoritative works on Yoga:*

"One who has rightly distinguished between the permanent and the impermanent; who has cultivated a feeling of dislike towards worldly pleasures; who, having acquired full mastery over his organs, physical and mental, feels an insatiable longing to free himself from this cycle of existence, has attained the first stage, Subechcha, or Longing for the Truth. He who has pondered over what he has read and heard and has realized it in his life has attained the second stage, Vicharana, or Right Inquiry. When the mind, having abandoned the many, remains steadily fixed on the One, he has attained the third stage, Tanumanasa, or the Fading Out of the Mind.

"Till now he is a sadhaka, or practicer. Having reduced his mind by the three previous stages to a state of pure sattva, when he recognizes the Truth directly within himself – "I am Brahman" – he is on the fourth stage, Sattvapatti, or Attainment of the State of Sattva. Here the Yogi is called Brahmavid [Knower of Brahman]. Till now he was practicing Samprajnata samadhi, or contemplation where the consciousness of duality still lingers.

"Henceforward the three remaining stages form the Asamprajnata samadhi i.e. having no consciousness of the triad: knower, knowledge, and the known. When the Yogi is unaffected by the siddhis that manifest themselves at this stage, he attains the stage called Asamsakti (being unaffected by anything). The Yogi is now called Brahmavidvara. Till now he goes about performing his necessary duties of his own will. But when he sees nothing but Brahman everywhere, that stage is called Pararthabhavani, i.e. where the external things do not appear to exist. Here the Yogi performs his functions prompted by another.

"He is called Brahmavaristha when he has attained the seventh and last stage during which he neither performs his daily duties himself nor prompted by others, but remains in a state of perpetual Samadhi."

The author of this work is said to have attained this stage, as his name Swatmarama indicates.

हठविद्यां हि मत्स्येन्द्रगोरक्षाद्या विजानते।
स्वात्मारामोऽथवा योगी जानीते तत्प्रसादतः॥ ४ ॥

(4) Matsyendra, Goraksha and others knew well the Hatha Vidya. The Yogi Swatmarama learnt it by their favor.

This is the beginning of an account of the lineage of those who received this knowledge. According to tradition, through the grace of Lord Siva, Yogi Matsyendra was a fish who was changed into a human being and received the Hatha Vidya from Lord Siva himself. Knowledge does not come from just anywhere. It is like milk, which comes only from the udders of a cow. You cannot milk the ear. It is the same with the guru. Knowledge may be everywhere, but you cannot get the knowledge from anywhere except through the guru-disciple lineage. So Siva taught Matsyendranath. Matsyendranath taught his disciple Gorakshanath, and through their grace eventually Swatmarama the author of this book learned Hatha Yoga. In Sanskrit this is called "guruparampara."

श्रीआदिनाथमत्स्येन्द्रशाबरानन्दभैरवाः।
चौरङ्गीमीनगोरक्षविरूपाक्षबिलेशयाः॥ ५ ॥

मन्थानो भैरवो योगी सिद्धिर्बुद्धश्च कन्थडिः।
कोरण्टकः सुरानन्दः सिद्धिपादश्च चर्पटिः॥ ६ ॥

कानेरी पूज्यपादश्च नित्यनाथो निरञ्जनः।
कपाली बिन्दुनाथश्च काकचण्डीश्वराह्वयः॥ ७ ॥

अल्लामः प्रभुदेवश्च घोडाचोली च टिण्टिणिः।
भानुकी नारदेवश्च खण्डः कापालिकस्तथा॥ ८ ॥

इत्यादयो महासिद्धा हठयोगप्रभावतः।
खण्डयित्वा कालदण्डं ब्रह्माण्डे विचरन्ति ते॥ ९॥

*(5-9) Siva, Matsyendra, Sabara, Anandabhairava,
Chourangi, Meena, Goraksha, Virupaksha, Bilesaya,
Manthana, Bhairava, Siddhi, Buddha, Kanthadi,
Korantaka, Surananda, Siddhapada, Charpati, Kaneri,
Pujyapada, Nityanatha, Niranjana, Kapalin,
Bindunatha, Kaka Chandeeswara, Allama, Prabhudeva,
Ghodacholin, Tintini, Bhanukin, Naradeva, Khanda,
Kapalika and many other great siddhas, having
conquered time by the power of Hatha Yoga, move
about the world.*

There are many Hatha Yoga masters. Just to hear their names is like
getting their blessings. Above are some of the Hatha Yoga masters who
attained the siddhis. They not only acquired powers, but more
importantly, they were able to transcend time and space and to wander
on all fourteen planes because they were able to take their prana into
the Sushumna. Sometimes they come to the physical plane to help
humanity, if you are ready for them. They could even keep their
physical body alive if they wanted to by bringing the prana into the
Sushumna. One can stop the decay of the physical person by stopping
the Ida and Pingala and activating the Sushumna. Such a person, one
whose energy moves through the Sushumna, is called a siddha. For
him there is no day or night, no birth or death.

The Buddha referred to above is not the Buddha most of you know
about. He is one of the Hatha Yoga masters.

अशेषतापतप्तानां समाश्रयमठो हठः।
अशेषयोगयुक्तानामाधारकमठो हठः॥ १०॥

(10) Hatha Yoga is a sheltering monastery for those scorched by all the (three) types of pain. To all those engaged in the practice of Yoga, Hatha Yoga is like the tortoise that supports the world.

Brahmananda's Commentary: *The three tapas are: adhyatmika, adhidaivika, and adhibhoutika. Adhyatmika is of two kinds, bodily and mental. Adhidaivika are those sufferings caused by planetary influences, and the adhibhoutika are those caused by tigers, serpents, etc.*

हठविद्या परं गोप्या योगिना सिद्धिमिच्छता ।
भवेद्वीर्यवती गुप्ता निर्वीर्या तु प्रकाशिता ॥ ११ ॥

(11) The Yogi desirous of obtaining siddhi should keep the Hatha Yoga very secret, for it is effective only when it is kept secret. It becomes vain when injudiciously revealed.

This is a warning to keep the knowledge secret. Do not reveal it to just anybody. It is a vidya – a knowledge – something not meant for everybody unless they are ready. When the student comes to the teacher, the teacher judges whether he is ready. Moreover, this is not something for idle broadcasting. It is just for yourself. Your practice should not be revealed to anybody else as they will not understand. It is not for a public demonstration.

Brahmananda's Commentary: *In this book Svatmarama describes these processes in detail, but still he says that the Yogi should keep it secret. So it is plain that everything is not revealed, and the most important processes are to be learned direct from the guru. Hence it follows that he who begins to practice this after a theoretical study of it and without a guru will come to harm. The adkari, or candidate, should have the following qualifications:*

(a) He should perform his duties and be free of personal
    motives and attachments.
(b) He should have perfected himself in yama and niyama
    (described later on), and cultivated the intellect. He should
    have conquered anger.
(c) He should be entirely devoted to his guru and
    the Brahmavidya.

No wonder that the masters refuse to admit all the candidates
indiscriminately, and say that an adept is the rare efflorescence
of an age.

Siddhi refers either to the eight siddhis, or psychic powers, or to
Kaivalya or Nirvana, which is the attainment of spiritual
perfection. The eight siddhis are: Anima, the power to assume a
minute form; mahiman, the power to assume an extensive
form; gariman, the power to become weighty; laghiman, the
power to become light; prapti, the power to reach the proximity
of even distant objects; prakamya, the power to obtain what is
desired; isita, the power to shape anything as desired; and
vasitva, the power to control anything.

सुराज्ये धार्मिके देशे सुभिक्षे निरुपद्रवे।
धनु:प्रमाणपर्यन्तं शिलाग्निजलवर्जिते।
एकान्ते मठिकामध्ये स्थातव्यं हठयोगिना॥ १२॥

(12) The practitioner of Hatha Yoga should live alone
in a small matha, or monastery, situated in a place
free from rocks, water, and fire to the extent of a
bow's length, and in a fertile country ruled over by a
virtuous king where he will not be disturbed.

Brahmananda's Commentary: 'Free from rocks, water and
fire'- These are considerations not to be passed over lightly by
anyone who wishes to pursue the ardous course of Yoga. By
'water' is meant here dampness or wetness.

The country should be one where the people are not gluttons, bandits or thugs. It must have a peaceful environment, one without terrorists, robbers or thieves. In a big city it is often dangerous to walk, but a country place is usually more suitable. "A country ruled over by a virtuous king" is one where the king is practicing dharma. Many countries are ruled over by dictators, and so they are places where it is legally forbidden to practice such things. I don't want to name them, but in certain countries you might be arrested for these practices. We must have full freedom to follow our practice without fear of disturbance.

You must also be situated in a place where food is available. You can't meditate or practice Hatha Yoga without sattvic foods such as lots of vegetables, fruit, and milk.

"Free from rocks, water, and fire": these are just very sensible instructions. The extent of a bow's length (how far an arrow can shoot) is maybe fifteen or twenty yards. Don't put your tent or other dwelling within twenty yards of a slope subject to falling rocks. Don't put your dwelling in an area subject to forest fires, earthquakes, or volcanoes. Don't put your tent near a swamp which will bring you the disturbances of mosquitoes and other pests. These are all sanitary considerations, not to be passed over lightly by anyone who wants to pursue this arduous course of Yoga.

अल्पद्वारमरन्ध्रगर्तविवरं   नात्युच्चनीचायतं
सम्यग्गोमयसान्द्रलिप्तममलं निःशेषजन्तूज्झितम् ।
बाह्ये   मण्डपवेदिकूपरुचिरं   प्राकारसंवेष्टितं
प्रोक्तं योगमठस्य लक्षणमिदं सिद्धैर्हठाभ्यासिभिः ॥ १३ ॥

(13) The matha should have a small door, and should be without any windows. It should be level and without any holes. It should be neither too high, too low, nor too long. It should be very clean, being daily smeared over with cow dung and should be free from all insects. Outside it should have a small hall

*with a raised seat and a well, and the whole should
be surrounded by a wall. These are the characteristics
of a yoga matha as laid down by the siddhas who
have practiced Hatha Yoga.*

Matha means hut (or it can be an ashram). It should not have windows
so wide that they might cause your mind to wander outside. Cow dung
was used in olden times in India when there was no cement for
flooring. When it was smeared over the bare earth floor, it dried to a
hard surface that prevented insects from entering. Even today it is used
in country places.

Brahmananda's Commentary: *If it is very high there will be
great difficulty in getting up, and if very long the eye will
wander far. Nandikeshwara adds to this: "The monastery
should be surrounded by flower gardens and groves so that the
eye of the Yogi resting on them might become calm. On the walls
of his room he should draw pictures of the cycles of existence and
the attendant miseries. He should depict a burning ground and
the narakas (the hells or places of purification after death) so
that the mind of the Yogi will conceive a dislike and distaste of
this worldly life."*

एवंविधे मठे स्थित्वा सर्वचिन्ताविवर्जितः ।
गुरूपदिष्टमार्गेण योगमेव समभ्यसेत् ॥ १४ ॥

(14) *Living in such a place, the Yogi, being free in
his mind from all cares, should practice only Yoga all
the time, as taught by his guru.*

It is not that the Yoga teacher is a babysitter, constantly watching. He
is guiding you. You should begin pranayama only with the guidance of
a guru. Otherwise you may not know the proper use of the diaphragm.

Merely studying all the books is not going to bring the desired result;
you must practice. Many people read the **Bhagavad Gita** or the

Ramayana and they don't practice. Others read the ***Bible*** and then afterwards go and smoke. Such a course of action won't take you anywhere. Practice is important.

The siddhis are obtained from Lord Siva only when you are not planning to use those powers. At that time they come to you automatically. The siddhis or knowledge are given only to one who has devotion to the higher Self, not to the ego or to the body. Devotion to the guru is necessary also because God and guru are one. As God will not come directly to help, He has to manifest through your teacher. According to the nature of the teacher, the disciple relationship takes place. Some gurus you may have for only one day. Gurudev Sivananda's teacher had to stay for only one hour because Sivananda had already practiced in past lives. He became a great master after just a little further practice. Then, years later, when he touched me, all my past knowledge came, and he made me a Hatha Yoga professor. Master did not sit with me and teach all these things. I had been practicing from his Sadhana Tattva before that, but his presence was needed to bring back those past memories.

A teacher is needed to awaken this knowledge from samskaras (subtle impressions) of past lives. You are not just born ignorant or blind. The teacher opens samskaras either by touch, smell, teaching, etc. In ancient times this was the most usual way for the teacher to teach.

The teacher himself must have also gone through this training and disciplined his life so that he can apply that regimen to you. He must know how much he can give you because he sees your evolution. He must prescribe just like a doctor: perhaps a certain amount of japa to help reduce an overly rajasic nature, etc.

> **Brahmananda's Commentary:** *The necessity of having a guru by one's side when practicing Yoga is here strongly dwelt upon. The **Yogabija** says, "He who wants to practice Yoga should have a competent guru with him. He should begin Pranayama only with the guidance of his guru." The work called **"Raja Yoga"** says, "Kaivalya is not to be got by any amount of study of the Vedas, shastras and tantras without the advice of a guru." In the **Skanda Purana** it is said, "The eight stages of Yoga are to be learnt only from a competent guru; the siddhis are to be obtained only from Siva." And Suresvaracharya declares that*

only through the Guru can the eightfold Yoga be learned.
["Eight stages" refers to Ashtanga (eight-limbed) or Raja Yoga.]
The srutis say, "The mahatmas reveal those things only to him
who has a deep devotion towards his higher Self and an equal
reverence towards his guru! Only he who has an acharya or
guru knows." The various standard books on Yoga are, I think,
meant not so much for beginners and students, as for gurus to
use as guidebooks to regulate their pupils' training. Even in
medicine, he who prescribes a course of treatment empirically,
without having thoroughly studied the nature and the
peculiarities of the patient's system, and without the ability to
see clearly the effect of the various medicines on the internal
organism, would be denounced as a quack and a charlatan. But
in Hatha Yoga, where the least mistake may end in death or
insanity, it is absolutely necessary to have with us a guru who
has passed successfully through the course, who can see clearly
through our system, and observe the effects of the various
processes and modify them accordingly.

अत्याहार: प्रयासश्च प्रजल्पो नियमग्रह:।
जनसङ्गश्च लौल्यं च षड्भिर्योगो विनश्यति॥ १५॥

(15) The yogi perishes by six causes: over-eating, hard
physical labor, too much talk, the observance of [unsuitable]
vows, promiscuous company, and unsteadiness.

These are warnings. Certain things will not bring you success; they will
not take you to the goal. Hard physical labor is one. When you are
practicing intense asanas and pranayama, you cannot cut wood for ten
hours. Just reduce it. A cold bath may be good at certain times, but not
during intense pranayama. It will shatter your nerves. At such times only
a warm bath is allowed. Also, you should not sit near a fire. Just as you
cannot overload yourself with food during this intense sadhana, you
may not fast for more than three to four hours at a time as this will
weaken the body. You should have a moderate, balanced, limited diet.
Do not go to extremes. Also, do not eat before going to bed at night,

because then in the early morning you will not be able to perform
pranayama properly.

> **Brahmananda's Commentary:** *The vows are such things as
> bathing in cold water early in the morning, taking meals [only]
> in the night, and fasting frequently.*

उत्साहात्साहसाद्धैर्यात्तत्त्वज्ञानाच्च निश्चयात् ।
जनसङ्गपरित्यागात् षड्भिर्योग: प्रसिध्यति ॥ १६ ॥

*(16) The yogi succeeds by six qualifications:
cheerfulness, perseverance, courage, true knowledge,
firm belief in the words of the guru, and by
abandoning unsuitable company.*

"True knowledge" is the knowledge that you are the Self (not the body),
at least theoretically.

> *[To do no harm, to speak the truth, to refrain from
> taking what belongs to another, to preserve
> continence, to practice forbearance and fortitude, to
> be merciful to all, to be straightforward, to be
> moderate in diet, and to purify oneself – these
> constitute Yama.]*

"Straightforwardly" means that in thought, word, and deed you
practice the truth. Preserving continence (full brahmacharya) is
especially important when you are practicing the intensive sadhana
described in this book. Then you will be successful. It will be explained
more a little later on. "Merciful" refers to ahimsa (non-violence).

> **Brahmananda's Commentary:** *All the above should be
> qualified to mean that we should avoid these acts in deed, word
> and thought.*

*[Tapas (austerities), cheerfulness, belief in God [astikya],
charity, worship of the deity, hearing the exposition of
Vedantic doctrines, shame, sound mind, japa (repeating
prayers), and vratas (observance of vows) – these
constitute niyama, the experts in Yoga say.]*

Brahmananda's Commentary: *These are clearly explained in*
Saindilya Upanishad *thus: "Tapas is the emaciation of the
body by the observances of fasts, etc. Cheerfulness means
contentment with what one obtains unasked. Astikya means a
belief in the Vedas and what they say. Charity means giving to
deserving persons with devotion what one has lawfully
acquired." On this point the* **Gita** *says: "Satvika dana or charity
consists in giving, to a person who cannot return it, in a proper
place and time, gifts simply as a matter of duty."*

*"Worship" should be performed with a calm and clear mind.
"Hearing" means the theoretical study of Vedanta. "Shame"
means repugnance to doing a thing prohibited by the Vedas and
Shastras. "Sound mind" implies devotion to the courses laid
down in the Vedas. "Japa" refers to practice of the mantras that
are not prohibited by the Vedas, as taught by the guru. It is of
two sorts, audible and internal. Internal japa is repeating the
mantras mentally.*

*The course of development here laid down seems the most
natural and at the same time the most effectual. ˙ The
attainment of yama and niyama comprises all the active and
the passive virtues. The four sadhanas are the necessary
qualifications of a pupil:*

*(a) Discrimination between the permanent and
     the impermanent.*
*(b) Perfect indifference to any objects of desire from the lowest
     forms of earthly life to that of the Demiurgeous.*
(c) Attainment of the six-fold qualities.
(d) Intense desire, and an intense striving, for emancipation.

All these are included in the first two stages of Yoga. By these means, the mind is naturally weaned away from any attachment to worldly objects, and consequently, is in a fair way to succeed in concentration. The asanas and pranayama come at the right time and remove any disturbing element arising from the body and its tendencies. The way to the higher paths is now smooth and easy.

But the ground is hard to tread, and very few have the pluck to go through it, or the patience to persevere under repeated failures. Therefore, nearly ninety-nine out of a hundred practitioners are frightened by the outlook and begin at the easiest and most practical point: asana and pranayama. They read of the magnificent and stupendous results laid down as following the easiest physical processes in an inconceivably short time, and take to it with avidity for some months. But finding that they do not see even a shadow of the glorious powers prophesied, they give up the whole effort in disgust and become the bitterest enemies of Yoga, denouncing it as false whenever they can get hearers.

These escape lightly, but others commit serious mistakes in the processes and end their lives as maniacs or suicides. They do not realize the important fact that these tremendous powers are promised as a result of a course of pranayama only when it is practiced by one who has perfected in himself the moral and the spiritual qualities included under yama and niyama. This point is beautifully brought out in the Yoga Vasistha in the following story:

"A sannyasi retired into the jungles and practiced pranayama for many years, but without realizing any of the powers foretold. He then went to a sage and reverently asked him to teach him Yoga. The sage told him to remain with him, and for the first two years met all his pupil's eager solicitations for instruction with 'Wait'. Gradually the sannyasi grew accustomed to the situation and forgot to trouble his master any more for instruction.

"At the end of twelve years the rishi one day called his pupil and asked him to pronounce the word 'Om.' When the sannyasi came to the first syllable, rechaka (exhalation) set in naturally. When he finished the second syllable, puraka (inhalation) set in. At the end of the third syllable, kumbhaka (retention) set in. As a spark of fire catches a whole field of sun-dried grass and the whole is in flame in a few minutes, so the pronunciation of the sacred word roused into activity the spiritual faculties that lay dormant hitherto in the pupil. In a short time he had passed the initial stages of pratyahara, dhyana and dharana, and settled into the pure and elated state of samadhi."

Our interest in the story lies in the fact that the sage patiently waited for the natural unfolding of his pupil's spiritual tendencies and the purifying of his nature through his association and surroundings. He chose the right time and, seeing into the nature of the pupil as into a glass, brought about, in a simple way, results psychical and spiritual, which persons who are unacquainted with the rationale of Yoga and without the guidance of a master, labor for years to obtain If these were understood and their importance fully realized, there would be fewer victims and failures

हठस्य   प्रथमाङ्गत्वादासनं   पूर्वमुच्यते ।
कुर्यात्तदासनं स्थैर्यमारोग्यं चाङ्गलाघवम् ॥ १७ ॥

(17) Asanas are treated of in the first place as they form the first stage of Hatha Yoga. Asanas that make one firm, free from diseases, and light of limb.

By now you understand that asanas are not all of Hatha Yoga; they are only the first stage.

Brahmananda's Commentary: *Asana is said to make one firm because it kills the Rajoguna that causes the fickleness of the mind. By removing diseases it facilitates concentration, for as Patanjali says, "Disease, dullness, doubt, carelessness, sloth, worldly-mindedness, false notion, missing the point, and instability, are the causes of the distraction of the mind, and they are the obstacles."*

Heaviness of body arises from a preponderance of Tamas, and asana removes this. Though it is impossible to explain clearly and realize the important truths that underlie the various Asanas, till the human system is understood in all its intricacy and detail, still it can be said that the various postures bring about many important results, physical and otherwise. For example, during some of them, various nerve centers are activized; these effectively help to control the irregularities in the body and what is more wonderful, but not less true, is the purification of our mental nature, i.e. the suppression of some of our animal passions. Several diseases brought on by an excess of or irregularity in the humours of the body – wind, bile and phlegm – are removed by the Asanas. Physiologist will find here a vast field for their researches.

वशिष्ठाद्यैश्च मुनिभिर्मत्स्येन्द्राद्यैश्च योगिभि:।
अङ्गीकृतान्यासनानि कथ्यन्ते कानिचिन्मया ॥ १८ ॥

(18) I proceed to give out some of the asanas that are accepted by such sages as Vasishta, and such yogis as Matsyendra.

Brahmananda's Commentary:: *Vasishta and Matsyendra were both jnanis and yogis, but the former was learned more in jnana and the latter in Yoga.*

जानूर्वोरन्तरे सम्यक्कृत्वा पादतले उभे।
ऋजुकायः समासीनः स्वस्तिकं तत्प्रचक्षते॥ १९॥

(19) *Having firmly inserted both insteps between the thighs and the calves of the legs, he should sit straight on a level place. This is Swastikasana.*

This is one of the meditative postures. Bend the right leg and bring the foot in. Do the same with the left, placing it above the right leg. Then place the toes of the left foot between the right calf and thigh.

सव्ये दक्षिणगुल्फं तु पृष्ठपार्श्वे नियोजयेत्।
दक्षिणेऽपि तथा सव्यं गोमुखं गोमुखाकृति॥ २०॥

(20) *Place the right ankle next to the left buttock and the left ankle next to the right buttock. This is called Gomukhasana, and resembles the face of a cow.*

एकं पादं तथैकस्मिन्विन्यसेदूरुणि स्थितम्।
इतरस्मिँस्तथा चोरुं वीरासनमितीरितम्॥ २१॥

(21) *Place one (the right) foot on the other (left) thigh and the other (left) foot on the (right) thigh. This is Virasana.*

So it becomes the Lotus pose.

गुदं निरुध्यच गुल्फाभ्यां व्युत्क्रमेण समाहित:।
कूर्मासनं   भवेदेतदिति   योगविदो विदु:॥ २२ ॥

*(22) Press the anus firmly with the
soles crossed and sit very carefully.
This is Kurmasana according
to the yogis.*

We call it Siddhasana. The above are the basic sitting poses.

पद्मासनं तु संस्थाप्य जानूर्वोरन्तरे करौ।
निवेश्य भूमौ संस्थाप्य व्योमस्थं कुक्कुटासनम्॥ २३॥

*(23) Assuming the Padmasana
posture, insert the hands between the
thighs and the calves. Planting them
[the hands] firmly on the ground, rise
from the ground. This is Kukkutasana.*

कुक्कुटासनबन्धस्थो दोर्भ्यां सम्बध्य कन्धराम्।
भवेत्कूर्मवदुत्तान   एतदुत्तानकूर्मकम्॥ २४॥

*(24) Assuming the Kukkutasana
posture, wind your arms around your
neck and remain raised like a
tortoise. This is called
Uttana Kurmasana.*

पादाङ्गुष्ठौ तु पाणिभ्यां गृहीत्वा श्रवणावधि।
धनुराकर्षणं   कुर्याद्धनुरासनमुच्यते॥ २५॥

(25) *Taking hold of both the toes with your hands, keep one arm extended and draw the other towards your ear as you would do with the string of a bow. This is called Dhanurasana.*

वामोरुमूलार्पितदक्षपादं   जानोर्बहिर्वेष्टितवामपादम्।
प्रगृह्य तिष्ठेत् परिवर्तिताङ्ग: श्रीमत्स्यनाथोदितमासनं स्यात्॥ २६॥

(26) *Place the right foot at the foot of the left thigh and the left foot outside the right knee. Take hold of the right foot by the left hand and the left foot by the right hand, and then turn your head towards the left completely. This is Matsyendrasana.*

मत्स्येन्द्रपीठं   जठरप्रदीप्तिं   प्रचण्डरुग्मण्डलखण्डनास्त्रम्।
अभ्यासत: कुण्डलिनीप्रबोधं चन्द्रस्थिरत्वं च ददाति पुंसाम्॥ २७॥

(27) *Matsyendrasana increases appetite by fanning the gastric fire, and destroys terrible diseases in the body. When practiced, it rouses Kundalini and makes the moon steady.*

Brahmananda's Commentary: *Above the root of the palate, the moon is said to be located, ever dropping cool ambrosial nectar that is wasted by mixing with the gastric fire. But this asana prevents it. There is a curious story told of Matsyendra. He is said to be the pupil of Adinath or Siva. Once Siva went to a lonely island, and thinking it uninhabited, taught his wife Parvati the mysteries of Yoga. A fish that happened to near the shore heard everything and remained immovable with its mind concentrated. Adinath perceiving this, thought that the fish had learned the Yoga, and being extremely merciful, sprinkled water upon him. Immediately he became a siddha, possessing a divine body, and was called Matsyendra.*

This is deeply symbolic and suggestive. Compare with the story of the Matsya Avatara, the fish to whose horn the Hindu ark of Vaivasvata was tied during the flood.

प्रसार्य पादौ भुवि दण्डरूपौ दोर्भ्यां पदाग्रद्वितयं गृहीत्वा।
जानूपरिन्यस्तललाटदेशो   वसेदिदं पश्चिमतानमाहुः॥ २८ ॥

(28) Stretch out both the legs, and having taken hold of the toes of the feet with the hands, place your forehead upon your knees. This is Paschimottanasana.

इति पश्चिमतानमासनाग्र्यं पवनं पश्चिमवाहिनं करोति।
उदयं जठरानलस्य कुर्यादुदरे कार्श्यमरोगतां च पुंसाम्॥ २९ ॥

(29) This most excellent of all asanas, Paschimotanasana, makes the breath flow through the Sushumna, rouses the gastric fire, makes the loins lean, and removes all diseases.

धरामवष्टभ्य   करद्वयेन   तत्कूर्परस्थापितनाभिपार्श्व:।
उच्चासनो दण्डवदुत्थित: स्यान्मायूरमेतत्प्रवदन्ति पीठम्॥ ३० ॥

*(30) Plant your hands
firmly on the ground and
support your body upon your
elbows, pressing against the
side of your loins. Raise your
feet in the air stiff and straight and on a level with
the head. This is Mayurasana.*

Brahmananda's Commentary: *This posture resembles the
plant balance in the modern course of gymnastics on the
parallel bars.*

हरति सकलरोगानाशुगुल्मोदरादी-
        नभिभवति च दोषानासनं श्रीमयूरम्।
बहु कदशनभुक्तं भस्म कुर्यादशेषं
        जनयति जठराग्निं जारयेत्कालकूटम्॥ ३१ ॥

*(31) This asana cures diseases of the stomach,
glands and spleen, and removes all diseases caused
by an excess of wind, bile, or phlegm. It easily digests
food taken immoderately and promiscuously, and
reduces to ashes even the terrible poison halahala.*

Brahmananda's Commentary: *During the churning of the
ocean by the gods and the asuras, the first thing that came out
was the poison Kalakoota or Halahala. It began to burn the
three worlds and no god could be persuaded to eat it. At last*

Siva swallowed it, but before it got down his throat, Parvati held it firmly. So it remained forever there, and Siva's throat became blue.   Hence his name Kalakantha or Neelakantha (blue-throated).   This plainly reveals some great cosmic mystery connected with the evolution of our planetary system.

उत्तानं शववद्भूमौ शयनं तच्छवासनम् ।
शवासनं श्रान्तिहरं चित्तविश्रान्तिकारकम् ॥ ३२ ॥

(32) *Lying upon one's back on the ground at full length like a corpse is called Savasana. This relieves the fatigue caused by the other asanas, and induces calmness of mind.*

चतुरशीत्यासनानि शिवेन कथितानि च ।
तेभ्यश्चतुष्कमादाय सारभूतं ब्रवीम्यहम् ॥ ३३ ॥

(33) *The asanas as given out by Siva are eighty-four in number. Of those, I shall describe four of the most important.*

Brahmananda's Commentary: *Goraksha says, "There are as many asanas as there are varieties of beings. Siva has counted eighty four lakhs [one lakh = 100,000] and only he knows them. Of these he has selected eighty four; among these, four are the most important and useful.*

सिद्धं पद्मं तथा सिंहं भद्रं चेति चतुष्टयम्।
श्रेष्ठं तत्रापि च सुखे तिष्ठेत् सिद्धासने सदा॥ ३४॥

(34) They are: Siddha, Padma, Simha, and Bhadra. Of these, the most comfortable and the most excellent is Siddhasana.

योनिस्थानकमङ्घ्रिमूलघटितं कृत्वा दृढं विन्यसे-
न्मेढ्रेपादमथैकमेव हृदये कृत्वा हनुं सुस्थिरम्।
स्थाणुः संयमितेन्द्रियोऽचलदृशा पश्येद् भ्रुवोरन्तरं
ह्येतन्मोक्षकपाटभेदजनकं सिद्धासनं प्रोच्यते॥ ३५॥

(35) Press firmly the perineal space with the heel and place the other heel above the penis (or pubic bones). Fix your chin tightly upon your breast. Remain erect with your organs under control and look fixedly at the spot between the eyebrows. This is called Siddhasana, and removes every obstacle from the path to emancipation.

मेढ्रादुपरि विन्यस्य सव्यं गुल्फं तथोपरि।
गुल्फान्तरं च निक्षिप्य सिद्धासनमिदं भवेत्॥ ३६॥

(36) Place the right heel above the penis and the left above the right. This is called Siddhasana also.

Brahmananda's Commentary: *The Siddhasana described in the previous slokas is practiced by the followers of Matsyendra. The one now described is preferred by other yogis.*

एतत् सिद्धासनं प्राहुरन्ये वज्रासनं विदु:।
मुक्तासनं वदन्त्येके प्राहुर्गुप्तासनं परे ॥ ३७॥

(37) Some say that this is Siddhasana, others Vajrasana, others Muktasana, and other Guptasana.

Brahmananda's Commentary: *That described first is called alike Siddhasana and Vajrasana. Muktasana consists in placing one heel under the perineal space and the other heel under it. Guptasana is described in stanza thirty-six above.*

यमेष्विव मिताहारमहिंसां नियमेष्विव।
मुख्यं सर्वासनेष्वेकं सिद्धा: सिद्धासनं विदु: ॥ ३८॥

(38) The siddhas say that as among niyamas, the most important is not doing any harm to anyone, and among yamas, a moderate diet, so is Siddhasana among the asanas.

चतुरशीतिपीठेषु सिद्धमेव सदाभ्यसेत्।
द्वासप्ततिसहस्राणां नाडीनां मलशोधनम् ॥ ३९॥

(39) Of the eighty-four asanas, one should always practice Siddhasana. It purifies the 72,000 nadis.

आत्माध्यायी मिताहारी यावद्द्वादशवत्सरम्।
सदा सिद्धासनाभ्यासाद्योगी निष्पत्तिमाप्नुयात् ॥ ४०॥

(40) The yogi practicing contemplation upon his Atman, and observing a moderate diet, if he practices the Siddhasana for twelve years, obtains fulfilment.

किमन्यैर्बहुभि: पीठै: सिद्धे सिद्धासने सति।
प्राणानिले सावधाने बद्धे केवलकुम्भके॥ ४१ ॥

(41) When the Siddhasana is mastered and the breath carefully restrained by the practice of Kevala kumbhaka, why do we need the various other asanas?

उत्पद्यते निरायासात्स्वयमेवोन्मनी कला।
तथैकस्मिन्नेव दृढे सिद्धे सिद्धासने सति।
बन्धत्रयमनायासात्स्वयमेवोपजायते॥ ४२ ॥

(42) When the Siddhasana is mastered, the Unmani avasta (described later on) that gives delight, the moon and the three bandhas follow without effort and naturally.

Brahmananda's Commentary: *The bandhas are: Mula bandha, Uddiyana bandha, and Jalandhara bandha. As these and the Unmani avasta are described later on, I refrain from explaining them here.*

नासनं सिद्धसदृशं न कुम्भ: केवलोपम:।
न खेचरी समा मुद्रा न नादसदृशो लय:॥ ४३ ॥

(43) There is no asana like the Siddha, no kumbhaka like the Kevala, no mudra like the Khechari, and no laya (absorption of the mind) like the Nada.

वामोरूपरि दक्षिणं च चरणं संस्थाप्य वामं तथा।
दक्षोरूपरि पश्चिमेन विधिना धृत्वा कराभ्यां दृढम्।
अङ्गुष्ठौ हृदये निधाय चिबुकं नासाग्रमालोकये-
देतद्व्याधिविनाशकारि यमिनां पद्मासनं प्रोच्यते॥ ४४॥

(44) *Place the right heel at the root of the left thigh and the left heel at the root of the right. Cross the hands behind the back and take hold of the toes, the right toe with the right hand and the left toe with the left. Place the chin firmly on the breast and look fixedly at the tip of the nose. This is called Padmasana and destroys all diseases.*

Brahmananda's Commentary: *The secret teaching is that there should be a space of three inches between the chin and the breast.*

उत्तानौ चरणौ कृत्वा ऊरुसंस्थौ प्रयत्नतः।
ऊरुमध्ये तथोत्तानौ पाणी कृत्वा ततो दृशौ॥ ४५॥

नासाग्रे विन्यसेद्राजदन्तमूले तु जिह्वया।
उत्तम्भ्य चिबुकं वक्षस्युत्थाप्य पवनं शनैः॥ ४६॥

(45, 46) *Another view: Place the feet firmly (soles up) on the opposite thighs and place the hands (palms up) one upon another in the middle. Direct your eyes to the tip of the nose*

*and place the tip of the tongue at the root of the
front teeth. Place the chin on the chest and slowly
raise upwards the prana (by contracting the anus in
the Mula bandha).*

इदं पद्मासनं प्रोक्तं सर्वव्याधिविनाशनम्।
दुर्लभं येन केनापि धीमता लभ्यते भुवि॥ ४७॥

*(47) This is Padmasana that destroys all diseases.
It cannot be attained by ordinary mortals. Only some
intelligent persons attain it.*

कृत्वा सम्पुटितौ करौ दृढतरं बद्ध्वा तु पद्मासनं
गाढं वक्षसि सन्निधाय चिबुकं ध्यायँश्च तच्चेतसि।
वारं   वारमपानमूर्ध्वमनिलं   प्रोत्सारयन्पूरितं
न्यञ्चन्प्राणमुपैति बोधमतुलं शक्तिप्रभावान्नर:॥ ४८॥

*(48) Assuming the Padmasana posture and having
placed the palms one upon another, fix the chin
firmly upon the breast and contemplating upon
Brahman, frequently contract the anus and raise the
apana upwards. By a similar contraction of the
throat, force the prana downwards. By this he
obtains unequalled knowledge through the favor of
Kundalini (which is roused by this process).*

Brahmananda's Commentary: *By the union of the prana and
the apana, the gastric fire is roused and the serpent Kundalini
(that lies coiled three and a half times round the Sushumna,
closing the opening with its mouth) feels this and begins to*

move, straightening itself and proceeding upwards. Then the
prana and the apana should be forced through the hole into the
Sushumna. The process described in this verse is that of
Jalandhara bandha.

पद्मासने स्थितो योगी नाडीद्वारेण पूरितम् ।
मारुतं धारयेद्यस्तु स मुक्तो नात्र संशय:॥ ४९ ॥

(49) The yogi, sitting in the Padmasana posture, by
restraining the breath drawn in through the nadis,
becomes liberated. There is no doubt of this.

गुल्फौ च वृषणस्याध: सीवन्या: पार्श्वयो: क्षिपेत् ।
दक्षिणे सव्यगुल्फं तुं दक्षगुल्फं तु सव्यके ॥ ५० ॥

(50) Then the Simhasana is described: Place the
ankles upon that part of the body between the anus
and scrotum – the right ankle upon the left side of it,
and the left ankle upon the right.

हस्तौ तु जान्वो: संस्थाप्य स्वाङ्गुली: सम्प्रसार्य च ।
व्यात्तवक्रो निरीक्षेत नासाग्रं सुसमाहित:॥ ५१ ॥

(51) Place the palms upon the knees,
extend the fingers and direct the eyes to
the tip of the nose with opened mouth
and a concentrated mind.

सिंहासनं भवेदेतत्पूजितं योगिपुङ्गवै:।
बन्धत्रितयसन्धानं कुरुते चासनोत्तमम्॥ ५२॥

*(52) This is the Simhasana held in so great esteem
by the highest yogis. This most excellent asana
facilitates the three bandhas.*

गुल्फौ च वृषणस्याध: सीवन्या: पार्श्वयो: क्षिपेत्।
सव्यगुल्फं तथा सव्ये दक्षगुल्फं तु दक्षिणे॥ ५३॥

*(53) Next the Bhadrasana: place
the ankles upon the sides of the
sivni (the part between the anus
and the scrotum) [the
perineum]. The right upon the
right and the left upon the left side.*

पार्श्वपादौ च पाणिभ्यां दृढं बद्ध्वा सुनिश्चलम्।
भद्रासनं भवेदेत्तत्सर्वव्याधिविनाशनम्॥ ५४॥

*(54) Then bind the thighs with your hands wound
around them. This is Bhadrasana and destroys
all ills. The siddhas and the yogis call
this Gorakshasana.*

गोरक्षासनमित्याहुरिदं वै सिद्धयोगिन:।
एवमासनबन्धेषु योगीन्द्रो विगतश्रम:॥ ५५॥

(55) Thus the yogi should untiringly practice all these asanas until he feels no pains or fatigue, purifying the nadis by performing pranayama and practice the mudras and kumbhakas of various sorts.

This is the main thing. After performing asanas, now you must purify the nadis, the nerves. That is what the second chapter instructs.

अभ्यसेन्नाडिकाशुद्धिं मुद्रादिपवनक्रियाम्।
आसनं कुम्भकं चित्रं मुद्राख्यं करणं तथा ॥ ५६ ॥

(56) Then in the course of Yoga, the concentration upon the nada (sounds which come from the Anahata chakra or the Cardiac plexus) comes next.

So after pranayama, we go into meditation. Here it takes the form of concentration on the inner sound. We will go into this later on.

अथ   नादानुसन्धानमभ्यासानुक्रमो   हठे।
ब्रह्मचारी   मिताहारी   त्यागी   योगपरायण:।
अब्दादूर्ध्वं भवेत् सिद्धो नाऽत्र कार्या विचारणा ॥ ५७ ॥

(57) The brahmachari (devotee of Brahman) who, leading a chaste life and observing a moderate diet, practices this Yoga, renouncing the fruits of his actions, becomes a siddha after a year. There need be no doubt about this.

For this you must practice all these things properly.

सुस्निग्धमधुराहारश्चतुर्थांशविवर्जितः।
भुज्यते शिवसम्प्रीत्यै मिताहारः स उच्यते ॥ ५८ ॥

(58) Moderate diet is defined to mean taking pleasant and sweet food, leaving one-fourth of the stomach free, and offering the act up to Siva.

Brahmananda's Commentary: He should fill two parts of his stomach with food and the third with water, leaving the fourth free for the passage of air. Pleasing Siva means that he should think that the eater is Siva and not himself. As the srutis say: "The eater is Maheswara, the great Lord."

कट्वम्लतीक्ष्णलवणोष्णहरीतशाकसौवीरतैलतिलसर्षपमद्यमत्स्यान्।
आजादिमांसदधितक्रकुलत्थकोलपिण्याकहिङ्गुलशुनाद्यमपथ्यमाहुः ॥ ५९ ॥

(59) The following things are considered as unsalutary to the yogis: things that are sharp, sour, pungent and hot, myrabolans, betel nut and leaves, the ordinary conjee oil, sesame or mustard oil, liquors, fish, flesh of animals like the goat, curds, buttermilk [not Western-style buttermilk, which is good for practice], fruit of the jujube, oil cakes, asafoetida, and garlic.

These things should be avoided during a course of intense pranayama such as this one.

Brahmananda's Commentary: By sharp things, bitter substances such as bitter gourd, etc. are meant; sour such as tamarind; pungent as chillies; hot such as those that increase the temperature of the body, as sugar, jaggery [natural sugar], salt.

भोजनमहितं विद्यात् पुनरस्योष्णीकृतं रूक्षम्।
अतिलवणमम्लयुक्तं कदशनशाकोत्कटं वर्ज्यम्॥ ६० ॥

*(60) Diet of the following nature should be avoided
as being unhealthy: food that having once been
cooked has grown cold and is heated again, that has
an excess of salt and sourness, that is indigestible,
and that has the leaves of the woody quassea
mixed with it.*

Food that has once been cooked should not be reheated as that will
drive out all its energy. This rule originated because there was no
refrigeration in India, and people would leave food from one meal to
the next and then reheat it – something very bad. Indigestible.

वह्निस्त्रीपथिसेवानामादौ   वर्जनमोचरेत्॥ ६१ ॥
तथाहि गोरक्षवचनम्–
''वर्जयेद्दुर्जनप्रान्तं   वह्निस्त्रीपथिसेवनम्।
प्रातः स्नानोपवासादि कायक्लेशविधिं तथा॥''

*(61) Goraksha says that he should avoid in the
beginning: bad company, basking near the fire during
winter, sexual relations and long journeys, bathing
early in the morning, fasting, and hard physical work.*

Basking near a fire will cause you to inhale carbon dioxide.

Brahmananda's Commentary: *By mentioning basking near
the fire, sexual intercourse, long journeys to sacred places by
foot, it should be understood that they should be avoided
during the period of practice. After one completely masters the*

*practice, he may (optionally) have recourse to basking near the
fire during winter, having sexual intercourse with his wife
during the proper time (as laid down in the smritis), and
making journeys by foot to sacred places, provided that he is a
grihastha (householder). That this is the view taken by the
author is clear from the verse quoted from Gorakshanath.
Bathing early in the morning brings on cold, and fasting and
such other practices require the exercise of the body, therefore
these should also be avoided. Fasting increases bile.*

गोधूमशालियवषाष्टिकशोभनान्नं   क्षीराज्यखण्डनवनीतसितामधूनि।
शुण्ठीपटोलकफलादिकपञ्चशाकं मुद्रादिदिव्यमुदकं च यमीन्द्रपथ्यम्॥ ६२ ॥

(62) *The following things can be safely taken by the
yogi: wheat, rice, barley, milk, ghee, sugar candy,
butter, honey, dry ginger, cucumber, the five
potherbs, kidney beans (payaran), and good water.*

Ghee is clarified butter. Sugar candy is a crystallized form of sugar.
Cucumber is one of the best things you can take. Your Western
spinach is one of the five potherbs mentioned.

पुष्टं सुमधुरं स्निग्धं गव्यं धातुप्रपोषणम्।
मनोऽभिलषितं योग्यं योगी भोजनमाचरेत्॥ ६३ ॥

(63) *The yogi should take a nourishing and sweet
food mixed with milk. It should be pleasing to the
senses and nutritive to the dhatus (humours).*

Brahmananda's Commentary: *The dhatus are seven in number. They are chyle, flesh, blood, bones, marrow, fat and semen.*

This is very important. We give it to our sadhana intensive students in the early morning to help their pranayama. It is very nourishing and not at all heavy.

युवा वृद्धोऽतिवृद्धो वा व्याधितो दुर्बलोऽपि वा।
अभ्यासात्सिद्धिमाप्नोति   सर्वयोगेष्वतन्द्रितः॥ ६४॥

(64) *Any person, if he actively practices Yoga, becomes a siddha.*

Anyone who is able to get control of the prana, be he young, old, or even very sickly and weak, can get success.

क्रियायुक्तस्य सिद्धिः स्यादक्रियस्य कथं भवेत्।
न शास्त्रपाठमात्रेण   योगसिद्धिः   प्रजायते॥ ६५॥

(65) *One who practices will obtain siddhis, but not one who is idle. Yoga siddhis are not obtained by a mere theoretical reading of the shastras.*

न वेषधारणं सिद्धेः कारणं न च तत्कथा।
क्रियैव कारणं सिद्धेः सत्यमेतन्न संशयः॥ ६६॥

(66) *Siddhis are not obtained by wearing the dress of a yogi,*

Merely wearing an orange robe and growing a beard will not do it; you
are still the same person underneath.

or by talking about them, but untiring practice is the
secret of success. There is no doubt about this.

पीठानि कुम्भकाश्चित्रा दिव्यानि करणानि च।
सर्वाण्यपि हठाभ्यासे राजयोगफलावधि ॥ ६७ ॥

(67) The various asanas, the kumbhakas, and the
various mudras of Hatha Yoga should be practiced
only so long as one does not attain Raja Yoga.

These should be practiced until the mind becomes very steady and the
prana goes into the Sushumna. Until then you must practice. Just
practice. Don't keep looking for a result; from practice and more
practice, eventually it will come. If you lift weights every day, little by
little your muscles will develop. It is the same here.

हठयोगप्रदीपिका

hatha yoga pradipika

CHAPTER TWO

अथासने दृढे योगी वशी हितमिताशनः।
गुरूपदिष्टमार्गेण प्राणायामान् समभ्यसेत्॥ १ ॥

*(1) The yogi, having perfected himself in the
asanas, should practice pranayama according to the
instructions laid down by his guru, with his senses
under control, observing all along a nutritious and
moderate diet.*

CHAPTER TWO

अथासने दृढे योगी वशी हितमिताशनः।
गुरूपदिष्टमार्गेण प्राणायामान् समभ्यसेत्॥ १ ॥

(1) The yogi, having perfected himself in the asanas, should practice pranayama according to the instructions laid down by his guru, with his senses under control, observing all along a nutritious and moderate diet.

चले वाते चलं चित्तं निश्चले निश्चलं भवेत्।
योगीस्थाणुत्वमाप्नोति ततो वायुं निरोधयेत्॥ २ ॥

(2) When the breath wanders, i.e., is irregular, the mind is also unsteady, but when the breath is still, so is the mind, and the yogi lives long. So one should restrain the breath.

How can the breath wander? We can understand this verse only when we realize that it is not the physical breath that is meant here, it is the prana. This confusion is due to the problems of translation. The original Sanskrit, "Prana Vayu," is here translated as breath because in English there is no word for prana. Sometimes it is translated as air, other times as breath. Because of possibilities of confusion such as this, a guru is necessary.

Mind is like a tree and breath is like the wind. We can't see the wind, but when we see the motion of the tree, we know that the air is disturbed. It is the same with thought. When the prana is disturbed or unsteady, your mind is so disturbed that you cannot sit quietly in one place. In the extreme case of a madman, the prana is so very disturbed that it is not being channelled properly (neither afferent nor efferent currents are moving correctly, and the motor or sensory nerves are out of control). Then thought and body actions are completely out of control and one talks, moves and laughs completely inappropriately. This also happens to all of us in different degrees whenever our minds are not completely steady – when "breath wanders." The important thing to understand here is that prana and mind are interconnected.

The Pradipika says that "One should restrain the breath," but you all know that if you do that literally you won't live long. Again, we see that we must translate breath as prana. When this prana is regulated so that it becomes rhythmic, then breath also becomes rhythmic. We can watch the physical breath to learn how the prana moves. From watching the leaves on the tree, we know whether the wind is from the north or from the south, whether its speed is eight knots or whether it is stormy. Similarly, by watching the physical breath, we can tell a person's mental condition. This is one of the principles upon which lie detector machines are based.

When you do pranayama you are regulating the impulse coming to the diaphragm in a proportional way (1:4:2). Impulses are always going from the brain to the rest of the body, as for example when I move my arm. You cannot see the impulse but you can see the motion. The muscle is controlled by the mind which sends the impulses through the nervous system to the muscles. It all depends upon thought as it is thought which controls the impulses.

By using the physical breath you are regulating the impulse of prana (and of apana as well). Then, with the contraction of Mula bandha you are trying to stop the impulse from going to the sexual and lower organs; you are bringing the energy up. You shut off the prana not only by holding the breath, but also by touching the chin to the chest. By putting pressure on various nerves, you control the cardiovascular system: the heart rate and the respiratory rate. When you put pressure

on the Muladhara chakra by pressing the anal sphincter muscle with
the heel and by sitting over that area, you are putting pressure on the
Kanda, the place where all the nerves are joined. This presses on the
apana, forcing it up. The prana is forced down by the chin lock. In this
way these two impulses are joined together. That is called Hatha Yoga,
the union of "ha" and "tha." We need to apply physical pressure as well
as to employ the mind and the breath. Breath, thought, and body are
all employed; then with all three together, you get full control.

It is said that if you are very advanced in Raja Yoga, you don't have to
go through this process. An advanced Raja yogi is one who can control
his thought; once you do that, you control everything – prana and the
body. But such a person is very rare. An advanced Raja yogi has full
control over the emotions: lust, anger, greed, hatred, jealousy, envy, fear.
Most of us need to practice Hatha Yoga in order to get to Raja Yoga.

The yogi is said to "live long" because he regulates the impulse coming
so that the breath slows. In proportion that breath slows, life is
prolonged, because then energy is burned up more slowly. Catabolic
and anabolic activity both go down, one is balanced, and so youth is
maintained for a long time.

यावद्वायुः स्थितो देहे तावज्जीवनमुच्यते।
मरणं तस्य निष्क्रान्तिस्ततो वायुं निरोधयेत्॥ ३ ॥

*(3) A man is said to live only so long as he has the
breath in his body. When the breath goes out, he is
said to be dead. So one should practice pranayama.*

Again, he is not talking about the physical breath, but about prana.

मलाकुलासु नाडीषु मारुतो नैव मध्यगः।
कथं स्यादुन्मनीभावः कार्यसिद्धिः कथं भवेत्॥ ४ ॥

(4) When the nadis are full of impurities, the breath does not go into the middle nadi, Sushumna. Then there is no attainment of the object nor arriving at Unmani avasta.

Modern people who read such things may think that the author is making a ridiculous statement, that he knows nothing about physiology or anatomy. How can breath possibly go into the nadi when everybody knows that it goes only into the lungs! But if you again translate "breath" as prana, as I have explained, then you will understand such things properly.

What are the "impurities" mentioned above? When you eat the wrong food, when you drink or smoke, the nervous system is loaded with impurities, creating resistance. At that time, if you do pranayama, the prana will not go into the Sushumna. If the breath doesn't go into the Sushumna nadi, then there is "no attainment of the object." What is meant by that? The "object" is the union of "ha" and "tha," the union that will lead to stillness of the mind. When the mind is still, Raja yogis say that the seer sees Himself. He sees Himself as "I Am."

Unmani avasta is Hatha Yoga samadhi through control of the prana. In Raja Yoga this same state is called Asamprajnata Samadhi. In Jnana Yoga it is called Nirvikalpa Samadhi or Turiya. In Bhakti Yoga it is called Bhava Samadhi or self-surrender. All are the same state.

During Unmani avasta the breath stops and the mind becomes so still that you see the Self. Avastha refers to a state of the mind. In this state there are no more waves (vrittis) in the mind because the prana is no longer working through the Ida and Pingala. So long as the prana operates through these nadis, there will be physical breathing and life force, emotions, and thoughts. Ordinarily we cannot stop this; it stops only when the prana goes in the Sushumna so that Ida and Pingala are dead. Then they are like a wire without any current.

शुद्धिमेति यदा सर्वं नाडीचक्र महाकुलम्।
तदैव जायते योगी प्राणसङ्ग्रहणे क्षम: ॥ ५ ॥

(5) *When all the nadis that are now full of impurities become purified, then only can the yogi successfully perform pranayama.*

"Successfully" means that the prana goes into the Sushumna. When the nadis are impure, prana will not go into the Sushumna, so we must begin by doing pranayama to purify the nadis. The more effort that takes place, the sooner will come purification; the rest comes automatically. Actually, most of the time we spend in purification.

प्राणायामं तत: कुर्यान्नित्यं सात्त्विकया धिया।
यथा सुषुम्नानाडीस्था मला: शुद्धिं प्रयान्ति च ॥ ६ ॥

(6) *So one should practice pranayama with a mind in which the sattvic element prevails*

The "sattvic element" prevails when you want to reach your Self, or God, and are not performing pranayama for getting siddhis or powers. If these were your goal, then it would be the rajo-guna which would predominate. But this would be like the left hand trying to dominate the right hand, when actually there is only one Self. So if I want to show that I am bigger than you, that's not power, it's only illusion, ignorance. We should be performing this sadhana in order to reach the Self.

until the Sushumna nadi is freed from the impurities.

That may take one life, ten lives, ten million lives, or just ten seconds – that's possible too. How do you know that you have awakened this purification? The first sign is contentment. Do you know what is contentment? If you started this practice, hoping to gain a mink coat, by the time you are finished, you don't need or want a mink coat. You don't want anything. You got what you were really looking for: peace and self-contentment. When a person achieves this, he doesn't have to go to a bar or a discotheque or a concert. He is content to just look at a tree or to sit in a bare room. He is satisfied in whatever conditions he finds himself. If there's no electricity, that's okay. If there's no hot water, it's all right. No sun today, okay. But if tomorrow suddenly a beautiful dinner and wonderful dishes were brought, that would be okay too. That's called contentment.

When you are contented you are not looking for something, expecting happiness only if you have such and such a thing. For example, only if the weather is good, are you going to be happy. Only if Swami Vishnu teaches you everything are you going to be happy; only if your husband buys you a mink coat are you going to be happy; only if your wife cooks a delicious meal are you going to be happy.

In that way, will you ever find happiness? No, because when you are depending on someone else, things can always go wrong, and they do. You can't expect the sun to come out just because you are not happy without it. But you can be happy within your Self. You can smile at the rain also. That's called contentment.

When the nadis are purified, your thoughts are no longer going from right brain to left brain, and left brain to right brain. There is balance, there are no more ups and downs. Usually our life swings like a pendulum: one day going this way – happy and jumping and joyful, the next day going that way. Like a yo-yo, back and forth and back and forth. But Yoga is a balanced state of mind. Then hot and cold are the same, victory and defeat the same, censure and praise the same, gain and loss the same. That's called contentment.

When the prana goes in the Sushumna, the first sign is contentment. You can be alone in a cave as I was, or if you have to come and work with people, that's all right too. One day I was in a cave in the Himalayas and I was contented. The next day I was in a five star hotel in London. A five star hotel is all right too, but that hotel was just a temporary abode and not the source of my contentment. In the cave there was no hot or even cold water. I had to melt snow for water. Every day I had to be careful with firewood as it was very hard to find and extremely expensive to buy. But that was okay – that was the way God wanted it. And even though everybody had gone and I was alone, I was contented, knowing that I was an independent person and I could be happy by myself.

This comes naturally when purification has taken place and the Kundalini is slowly moving in an upwards direction. In the downward direction it is a yo-yo. This is how you will know it. As an example, suppose after eating a full meal, suddenly you were brought more food, what would you do? You wouldn't care about it, because the desire for food is gone. It is the same with purification of the nadis. It comes automatically.

When peace and contentment come to you, it means that the Kundalini is awakened or the Shakti is opened. Then you radiate this peace. Your friends and your family will see something new in you – a peaceful and calm face. They will sense a new atmosphere. They will feel just like a cold person coming from outside and warming himself in front of a fireplace. If you feel this contentment, others will also feel it. But even if others don't feel it, you are not unhappy about it because everyone is not going to praise you. Some people are going to criticize you anyway. That's the way the world is – the world of duality. No one ever is always praised in this world by everybody. Can you tell me of just one person who was praised by everybody? Was Moses praised by everybody? Even after forty years, among his own people there were many who revolted against him. Did everyone praise Jesus? They crucified him even though he was talking about peace and love. Similarly, Krishna, Rama, Buddha and Socrates were criticized. Swami Sivananda was criticized by his disciples; someone even brought an axe against him.

Your happiness should not be depending on outside influences. It is not ego if you have confidence in your own Self. Confidence in the Self means that you are seeing that one Self in everything as all are one. Then you know that there's nothing to please. The moment you are really satisfied with your life, it means that your Kundalini has awakened and your Sushumna is purified.

> **Brahmananda's Commentary:** *"Breath" does not mean the air taken in and given out, but the prana, i.e. the magnetic current of the breath. It would be absurd if we say that the breath should be made to go to the right toe, etc. In the preceding sloka, "sattvica buddhi" means a mind in which the rajasic elements such as unsteadiness, and tamasic elements such as sloth, etc., have been overcome by the worship of Ishwara and perseverance.*

बद्धपद्मासनो योगी प्राणं चन्द्रेण पूरयेत्।
धारयित्वा यथाशक्ति भूय: सूर्येण रेचयेत्॥ ७॥

*(7) The yogi assuming the Padmasana posture,
should draw in the prana through Ida, the left nostril,
and having retained it as long as he can, exhale it
through Pingala, the right nostril.*

प्राणं सूर्येण चाकृष्य पूरयेदुदरं शनै:।
विधिवत्स्तम्भकं कृत्वा पुनश्चन्द्रेण रेचयेत् ॥ ८॥

*(8) Again inhaling the prana through Pingala, he
should perform kumbhaka [retention] as laid down
in the books, and should again slowly exhale it
through Ida.*

येन त्यजेत्तेन पीत्वा धारयेदतिरोधत:।
रेचयेच्च ततोऽन्येन शनैरेव न वेगत: ॥ ९॥

*(9) He should perform puraka (inhalation) through
the same nostril by which he performed rechaka
(exhalation), and having restrained the breath to the
utmost, until he is covered with perspiration or until
his body shakes, should exhale it slowly and never
fast, as that would diminish the energy of the body.*

प्राणं चेदिडया पिबेन्नियमितं भूयोऽन्यया रेचयेत्।
पीत्वा पिङ्गलया समीरणमथो बद्ध्वा त्यजेद्वामया।
सूर्याचन्द्रमसोरनेन विधिनाऽभ्यासं सदा तन्वतां
शुद्धा नाडिगणा भवन्ति यमिनां मासत्रयादूर्ध्वतः॥ १० ॥

(10) Draw in the prana by the Ida and exhale it by the Pingala. Again, draw it in through the Pingala, and having retained it as long as you can, exhale it through the Ida. The yogi who has perfected himself in yama by practising pranayama through the right and left gets his nadis purified in not less than three months.

This is Anuloma Viloma [Alternate Nostril Breathing]. In three months you can achieve a certain degree of purification. There will be satisfaction, peace and contentment. All this will come, provided you have this qualification: observance of yamas and niyamas. Merely practising left and right breathing alone is not sufficient.

What are the niyamas? They are the following observances:

1) Saucha – cleanliness, both internal and external: internal cleaning through Neti and Dhauti, and a sattvic, pure vegetarian diet.
2) Santosha – contentment (discussed before), where you are satisfied in whatever situation you are. Some person may be born in a big palace and another may be born in a slum. What is the cause behind it? Karma. It is our own actions from the past which cause reaction. So you should be contented no matter what situation you are thrown into.
3) Tapas – penance (fasting, taking vows such as performing a certain number of asanas, pranayamas, or eating only a certain type of food). Not foolish vows like standing in the cold water for ten hours and sitting in the hot sun near a burning fire. Some foolish people do these things, but that's torture and it's against Yoga. True yogis won't do that type of tapas. Torturing the body in the

name of God is not allowed. Neither is surrounding the body with too much luxury. Follow the middle path: not too much luxury, not too much suffering.

4) Swadyaya – study of the scriptures.
5) Ishwarapranidana – surrender to the will of God or surrender of the ego.

These are the yamas, or restrictions:
1) Satyam – telling the truth.
2) Ahimsa – non-violence.
3) Brahmacharya – celibacy.
4) Asteya – non-covetousness.
5) Aparigraha – non-receiving of presents.

Once the yamas and niyamas are established, then you perform pranayama. Only under this condition will you get the purification within three months. Anyone can practice pranayama, but if yama and niyama are not there, success will not come easily because mind will not be going in the right direction. But if those conditions are met, you can get the benefits even now; a tremendous inner awakening may come at any time.

प्रातर्मध्यन्दिने सायमर्धरात्रे च कुम्भकान्।
शनैरशीतिपर्यन्तं चतुर्वारं समभ्यसेत्॥ ११॥

(11) He should perform kumbhakas [retentions] four times a day: in the early morning, midday, evening, and midnight,

This means that at these four times during the day one should practice this inhalation, retention, exhalation, until perspiration comes. As the proportions are increased, you will feel perspiration coming out.

until he increases the number to eighty.

That's forty rounds, one round containing two retentions. Forty rounds make eighty retentions. Inhale, retain, exhale is half a round;

and then another inhale, retain, exhale makes one round. Forty rounds in the morning, forty at midday, forty in the evening, and forty at midnight. A beginner will start with ten or fifteen rounds and then continue until he reaches forty rounds.

During that period you should avoid salty things, as well as pungents, taking mostly sattvic foods such as milk, almonds, cooked rice in milk, ghee, etc. Taking this sattvic food and practicing with yama and niyama, along with the right attitude, will bring purification of the nadis within a few months. Then you will be shining like a bright lotus.

In addition to pranayama practice, you also have to spend time for morning asanas, evening asanas, morning meditation, evening meditation. Then you must have time for bandhas and mudras, study of the scriptures and for singing kirtan. As you must also make time to attend to your natural calls, etc., you might wonder where is the time for sleeping? If you follow this practice, your sleep will come automatically and you won't need much because only one or two hours of sleep will give you perfect rest. Then sleep becomes very deep and undisturbed.

But I am not recommending that you go as fast as that. If you do that now, in your present condition, the kickback will be tremendous. You will be disgusted: "Ugh, I didn't get anything that Swami mentioned." Start slowly and build up.

I recommend that you practice only three times daily, omitting the midnight practice. You will be getting almost the same benefit without going to that extreme. Really, this is the standard yogic way. When we go into seclusion, this is the way we practice.

If you live in hot climates such as Israel, it is the midday practice which should be omitted. Too much perspiration. Also, I suggest that you avoid extremely cold climates. Some extremists have even practiced pranayama while sitting in the snow, but don't practice this type of pranayama or you will have a complete breakdown of your nervous system. Everything should be moderate: not too cold and not too warm. Moderation is very important.

Brahmananda's Commentary: *This comes to about 320 kumbhakas daily. But as it might be inconvenient to practice at midnight, it might amount to 240 kumbhakas.*

कनीयसि भवेत्स्वेदः कम्पो भवति मध्यमे।
उत्तमे स्थानमाप्नोति ततो वायुं निबन्धयेत्॥ १२॥

(12) In the first stage, the body perspires.

There are three stages of purification. The first stage is intense perspiration. When you get perspiration, don't wipe it with your cloth. Instead, rub the sweat into the body with your hand. That sweat is magnetized because of the prana.

In the second [stage], a tremor is felt throughout the body.

The purification continues, and after three or four months of this Alternate Nostril Breathing, Ujjayi, etc., you start Bhastrika. Then the body will show, by way of various signs, that the second stage of purification has been reached. The signs will differ from person to person. The body may start moving so violently up and down that you are unable to control it, indicating that the prana is moving. Some people may experience a tremendous tremor of emotion, others will be more in a still state, some may fall into a kind of swoon, a semiconscious or even an unconscious state. Any of these indicate that the second stage of pranayama has been reached by the yogi who practices yama, niyama and right diet.

Only with these conditions is it good if you enter into this stage. But if you try to create this situation without yama, niyama, right diet, etc., you can rest assured that many reactions will come which you will not be able to control, and nobody will be able to help you. Doctors will not understand. From wrong practice, you might sometimes feel tremendous heat all over the body which a thermometer will not register. Nevertheless, you may feel as if you are on fire. Once in India, a student came up to me and said, "Swamiji, help me, the body is on fire." This was because he was not doing certain things properly, causing these negative reactions to come.

But if the tremor takes place, and if it is the right thing, then you feel at peace inside, and strong. The body may be moving violently but you are peaceful inside. The common reaction is always a blissful inner state. You will want to enjoy that state, to stay in that state. If you get that peaceful experience, you don't have to worry. But when the inner feeling is painful or if it is a negative state, then something is wrong. That is the surest way to find out whether you are progressing or whether you are going in the wrong direction.

In the highest stage, the prana goes to the Brahmarandhra. So one should perform pranayama.

Randhra means "canal," so Brahmarandhra is "Brahma's Canal." Where is Brahma's Canal? The Sushumna. With this third and highest stage of purification, the tremor will stop and there will be no more perspiration, though your energy is very high. You won't feel anything except the stillness of mind and that inner joy and happiness and peace.

Additional experiences will differ from person to person. Some people may see lights or colors, some may get more vibration in the spinal chord, others won't feel vibration or light anywhere. So if this happens to you, don't think that you are not progressing. These are just individual reactions due to differences in mental states from person to person. When the Kundalini is awakened, outward experiences will differ. These things are not important. The important thing is: are you peaceful? Are you satisfied with your life? Do you know that you are a free man? Do you have the freedom to do what you like now? Are your senses under your control? Is your mind no longer asking you to go to the pizza parlor to find happiness? These are the questions you should be asking. It is the inner experience you should be concerned with, not the external.

Occasionally blockages in the nadis occur as reactions to the taking of drugs, meat, alcohol and so forth, while following this practice. Blocking can take place, not only in the Sushumna nadi, but even in the Ida and Pingala (the normal channels), or in any of the fourteen major nadis, or even in any of the other 72,000 nadis. During blockage prana moves like a wild river, flowing into every nook and corner, going in any direction out of control. At that time it is very difficult to help such people. They never follow instructions, insisting on practicing bandhas, mudras, etc., without adequate preparation. They must first return to normal by changing their diet and other bad practices, and only then can they begin over with simple deep breathing exercises. They should not practice retention in the beginning. Then slowly, slowly, as the body becomes normal and the channels purify, then perhaps, after several months they can introduce alternate nostril breathing with retention. But help is very difficult to find for people in such trouble unless they come across a teacher who has had experience of these things and will understand immediately by looking at the person and know how to prescribe.

> **Brahmananda's Commentary:** *In the first stage, the prana is retained for twelve matras.*

That is the time when perspiration comes.

> *In the second [stage] twenty-four matras, and in the third, thirty-six matras. A matra is defined to be the time taken for circling the knee three times or flipping the fingers once.*

The ancients didn't have watches. For them the smallest unit was a matra, which is approximately three seconds. So in the first stage the prana is retained for thirty-six seconds (twelve matras); let us say that it is equal to a half minute.

> *Others say that a matra is the time occupied by clapping the hands thrice. A third definition is the time taken for the breath to go in and come out in the case of a man who is sound asleep.*

They used various definitions.

> *The first stage of pranayama has a period of twelve and a half breathings. Six such breaths are called "pala." The other stages of Yoga: pratyahara, dharana, dhyana, and samadhi, are only progressions in pranayama.*

Here they are not talking about physical breathing, but about the prana which is in the Sushumna. When the prana stays in the Sushumna for one and a half minutes, that is called "one breathing," or "one pala." When the prana stays in the Sushumna for more than twelve and a half breathings, it is no longer pranayama, but pratyahara.

There are three stages in the purification of the nadis. In the first stage, perspiration takes place. At that time, the prana is held for twelve matras (approximately 30 seconds). Notice that prana is held, not breath. You hold the prana for thirty seconds in the Sushumna. Prana will not stay for more than a certain time because there is a tremendous resistance there. It's like bringing together the same poles of two magnets: they will repel each other. In the same way, the positive force of the Sushumna and the not-so-purified energy of the Ida and Pingala are coming and pushing against each other. There is a temporary suspension for a very short time. That is called the first stage. So be sure to remember that "thirty seconds" does not mean that we are holding the physical breath. That is what is meant by "holding the breath in the Sushumna."

The second stage is held for twenty-four matras. In the third stage, the prana stays in the Sushumna for thirty-six matras (about one and a half minutes), but the true inner feeling of that time appears to be an eternity. Then there is no more time; you are not even aware that the world has any meaning. When you come out of that state, then you know that the world is like a mirage. Don't think that this experience takes place only in the Sushumna. Actually, you feel this radiation throughout your body, and not in a specific location. Location is given only so that your mind can concentrate. It is the same when you focus on chakras so that you can get more concentration power. This helps the energy to flow in the correct channel, which is the most important thing for bringing peace. This is what is meant by "holding the prana" in the different stages.

A word of caution: never take anything literally in Yoga. For example, the symbol of Lord Siva is the dancing Nataraja, representing creation and destruction, the dance of matter. Matter changes every moment. When one particle of matter dies, it becomes new matter for something else. That's called the "Dance of Siva." The petals on chakras are also symbols, hinting at energy pattern radiations. Such things are given so that the mind can visualize. They are just aids for focusing your concentration, so don't get stuck. Use the visualization to come into reality. In reality you never see petals in the chakras.

What you see are the energy pattern changes, the wavelength changes. For at these higher stages of practice you have a different type of experience. These symbols are just aids for focusing your concentration. Many yogic students make the mistake of taking these symbols literally, and when they don't get these experiences, they think that the teachings are all wrong. But that is because they have never approached their teacher to get a proper understanding of them.

In the third stage when certain energies start developing, you may start writing poetry. As the chakras develop, you may see clairvoyantly, or develop various powers, or you may only have the inner peace, not wanting to move, withdrawing from everybody. Reactions will be different, but the inner experience always remains the same: all will have experience of peace and joy

> **Brahmananda's Commentary:** *When the prana is restrained for a period of 125 palas, then it goes into Brahmarandhra. When the prana stays in Brahmarandhra for about twenty-five palas, that is pratyahara. If it remains there for five ghatikas (two hours), it is dharana. If it stays for sixty ghatikas (two and a half days), it is dhyana. If it is restrained for twelve days, it is samadhi.*

Again I want to emphasize that we are not talking about the physical breathing but about how long the prana stays in the Sushumna. With twelve and a half palas the prana stays only in the lower chakras, and then at about twenty or thirty palas it goes to the higher chakras. At about 120 palas it reaches the crown. That means that progression in the time of retention will cause the prana to go higher and higher.

Do not expect this to happen in one or two courses or by correspondence, even though it is actually your natural state. It may happen today, tomorrow, or progress might stagnate if you are careless. Now there may be enthusiasm, but if, the moment you finish this Intensive Course, you are be tempted by ice cream, pizza, boys and girls, dance and music, and sensual pleasures, then you are finished – the vairagya (dispassion) will be gone. The things you learn from your practice increase your vibratory level; they create a fire. Then it is like taking a glass of water, pouring it over the fire and putting it out.

You will have to start over again. With fits and starts like this you will not progress very much. What you need is continuous practice. Do not go too fast, such as morning, midday, night, and midnight for three months, and then nothing for three years. If you take that intense an approach there will be a reaction. It is like a man who lifts weights too much and too soon – after five minutes he will have to stop because of aching muscles, and the aching will persist even after he returns home, with the result that he abandons his weightlifting. Also with too much pranayama there will be a mental kickback; the mental pain will be tremendous. Many people are forced to leave the practice because they go too fast and the pain becomes unbearable for them.

This has happened to many students. They go too fast and then hit a roadblock. They stop and then go back to their old rut and stagnate there. In the next life they will have to start all over again, though coming again very quickly to that state where they left off. But if they have not developed viveka and vairagya, they will slip back once more. So, if you are practicing only ten pranayama a day, practice ten pranayama; if you are meditating for half an hour a day, continue. Eventually there will be an awakening. If you practice like that – little by little, every day, then the cumulative effect will be much better than a fast few months' work followed by no work at all. Continuous practice is best.

जलेन श्रमजातेन गात्रमर्दनमाचरेत् ।
दृढता लघुता चैव तेन गात्रस्य जायते ॥ १३ ॥

(13) Rub well on the body the perspiration given out. This gives firmness and lightness to the whole constitution.

In the first stage when you get perspiration, you should rub it well on the body – don't wipe it off. It is a pranic massage when you do that.

अभ्यासकाले प्रथमे शस्तं क्षीराज्यभोजनम् ।
ततोऽभ्यासे दृढीभूते न तादृङ्नियमग्रह : ॥ १४ ॥

*(14) In the early stages of practice, he should take
food mixed with milk and ghee. But when he has
advanced he need not observe such restrictions.*

In the early stages when you are purifying, you must take only food
mixed with rice and ghee. You must avoid such things as salt or spices.
This you should observe very strictly.

यथा सिंहो गजो व्याघ्रो भवेद्वश्य: शनै: शनै:।
तथैव सेविते वायुरन्यथा हन्ति साधकम् ॥ १५ ॥

*(15) As we tame lions, elephants and tigers
gradually, so also should prana be brought under
control. Else it will kill the practitioner.*

Have you ever seen a tiger in the circus? How are they trained? Very,
very slowly and carefully, watching every evidence of the cat's moods.
And what is the purpose of the chair held in front of the tiger? It is not
only for protection. When the tiger uses his claw on the chair, the chair
doesn't react, and so the tiger, thinking that the chair is a part of the
man's body, is fooled into thinking that the man is stronger than he is.
So even though the tiger is actually stronger, he is subdued by the
man's intellect.

It is the same with the prana. You must try to control the prana slowly.
A violent method, one too fast or without proper diet and other
essential conditions, will cause reactions. Just like an improperly
handled lion or tiger, it will injure you. This stanza is a warning not to
play with prana without following all the rules and regulations.

प्राणायामादियुक्तेन सर्वरोगक्षयो भवेत्।
अयुक्ताभ्यासयोगेन सर्वरोगसमुद्भव:॥ १६॥

(16) By the practice of pranayama (along with right food and proper bandha), one is freed from all diseases. By a mistaken course of Yoga, the yogi brings upon himself all diseases.

So either you can get rid of all diseases, or you can get all diseases, depending on how you are practicing.

हिक्काश्वासश्च कासश्च शिर:कर्णाक्षिवेदना:।
भवन्ति विविधा रोगा: पवनस्य प्रकोपत:॥ १७॥

(17) By a wrong course of pranayama, the breath becomes deteriorated, and hence cough, asthma, pains in the head, eyes, ears and various other diseases arise.

Asthma is a breathing difficulty, but this difficulty is not caused by the lungs. It arises because the prana comes to the respiratory system irregularly and also in the wrong direction. The diaphragm or other muscles may be contracting instead of expanding, or the breathing may be too shallow or otherwise incorrect. It is the same with sneezing and coughing – they are nothing but the motion of prana.

Mistaken practices of pranayama which cause disturbances in the prana will cause many types of sickness. That is why you are warned to be careful. The intention is not to frighten you, but to have you practice with care. It is like using a chainsaw; you must know how to operate it or you might cut yourself badly.

युक्तं युक्तं त्यजेद्वायुं युक्तं युक्तं च पूरयेत्।
युक्तं युक्तं च बध्नीयादेवं सिद्धिमवाप्नुयात्॥ १८॥

(18) He should gradually inhale the breath and as gradually exhale it; he should also restrain it gradually.

Not beyond capacity. Only by practicing inhalation, retention, and exhalation in a proportional way do you get control over the prana.

Thus it is that a man obtains siddhis.

यदा तु नाडीशुद्धिः स्यात्तथा चिह्नानि बाह्यतः।
कायस्य कृशता कान्तिस्तदा जायेत निश्चितम्॥ १९॥

(19) When the nadis are purified, the consequent signs are perceptible, i.e. the body becomes slender and bright.

You don't feel that the body is heavy. We are not talking about physical heaviness. You will almost feel that you are about to fly all the time (without wings of course). Light and clean. And there is a radiation – the skin, face and eyes all will be radiating and sparkling. This shows that the nadis are purified.

यथेष्टधारणं वायोरनलस्य प्रदीपनम्।
नादाभिव्यक्तिरारोग्यं जायते नाडिशोधनात्॥ २०॥

(20) If the nadis are purified, he is able to restrain his breath longer. The gastric fire becomes more

active, the nada (inner sound) is heard, and he
enjoys perfect health.

If the breath is restrained for a longer time (we are not talking about the physical breath), the prana goes into the Sushumna and then there is a balance between the right and the left hemispheres of the brain. Then also both the Ida and Pingala nadis are functioning alternately. That is what is meant by "restraining the breath."

When the gastric fire becomes more active you can eat even poison. Some people hear the nada (inner sounds), others are more likely to see lights, while still others may feel a kind of peace, a silence. Their mind doesn't want to move or hear anything at all – it just wants to rest in that experience of peace or silence. The external experience will manifest differently from person to person, but in all the stages, whether you perceive colors, lights, or sounds, one thing is common to all: the mind is very calm and peaceful. That is the central point which indicates that the nadis are purified. On the other hand, when there is no peace and the mind is constantly wandering, you are unhappy, or in a dejected mood, this shows that the prana is not moving properly because the nadis are unpurified.

मेद-श्लेष्माधिक: पूर्वं षट्कर्माणि समाचरेत्।
अन्यस्तु नाचरेत्तानि दोषाणां समभावत:॥ २१॥

(21) One who is of a flabby and phlegmatic
constitution should first practice the six acts [kriyas].
Others should not, as they have not these defects, the
three humours (wind, bile, and phlegm) being equal
in them.

With some people, their nose is running day and night or they are coughing morning and evening. Others are unable to digest food properly because of constant irritation in the stomach. Such people should first practice the six kriyas before beginning intense pranayama. The six kriyas are: Neti, Dhauti, Basti, Tratak, Nauli, and Kapalabhati. (Other kriyas, such as Kunja Kriya, which are long practices, are unnecessary for most people unless they have some specific diseases that call for them.) However, all can benefit from the practice of Jala neti or Sutra neti to keep the nostrils clean. Occasionally you can clean your stomach with salt water and then vomit it out. Kapalabhati, of course, all should practice regularly.

धौतिर्बस्तिस्तथा नेतिस्त्राटकं नौलिकं तथा।
कपालभातिश्चैतानि षट्कर्माणि प्रचक्षते॥ २२॥

(22) The six acts [or kriyas] are Dhauti, Basti, Neti, Tratak, Nauli, and Kapalabhati.

कर्मषट्कमिदं गोप्यं घटशोधनकारकम्।
विचित्रगुणसन्धायि पूज्यते योगिपुङ्गवैः॥ २३॥

(23) These six acts that purify the body should be carefully kept secret, as they produce various wonderful results and, as such, they are held in high esteem by the great yogis.

Such things as the kriyas are not generally given to ordinary people. They are kept secret because they are not meant for public demonstrations.

चतुरङ्गुलविस्तारं हस्तपञ्चदशायतम्।
गुरूपदिष्टमार्गेण सिक्तं वस्त्रं शनैर्ग्रसेत्।
पुन: प्रत्याहरेच्चैतदुदितं धौतिकर्म तत्॥ २४॥

(24) Take a clean piece of cloth 4 fingers broad and fifteen spans long [or 15 feet] and slowly swallow it according to the instructions of the guru.

Brahmananda's Commentary: *A long strip of cloth taken from a new muslin cloth would do well. Swallow a span the first day and increase it daily by a span. The cloth should also be a little warm.*

कासश्वासप्लीहकुष्ठं कफरोगाश्च विंशति।
धौतिकर्मप्रभावेण प्रयान्त्येव न संशय:॥ २५॥

(25) Draw it out again. This is called Dhauti, and removes asthma, splenetic diseases, leprosy and other diseases brought on by phlegm.

नाभिदघ्नजले पायौ न्यस्तनालोत्कटासन:।
आधाराकुञ्चनं कुर्यात् क्षालनं बस्तिकर्म तत्॥ २६॥

गुल्मप्लीहोदरं चापि वातपित्तकफोद्भवा:।
बस्तिकर्मप्रभावेण क्षीयन्ते सकलामया: ॥ २७॥

(26, 27)   Seat yourself in a vessel of water covering your navel, resting your body on the forepart of your feet, the heels resting against the posteriors. Insert a small bamboo tube into the anus. Then contract the anus (so as to draw the water in) and shake well the water within the stomach (and dispel it). This is Basti. By the power of Basti splenetic diseases, dropsy and other diseases arising from an excess of wind, bile and phlegm are cured.

This is called Basti. When you perform Nauli under these conditions, water is drawn up automatically.

Brahmananda's Commentary: *The bamboo tube should be six fingers long and four finger lengths of it should be inserted in the anus.   Some practice without this tube, but it is very dangerous as all the water does not come out and so causes many diseases.   The above two processes should not be gone through after a full meal, nor should one delay taking his meals after these.*

धात्विन्द्रियान्त:करणप्रसादं दद्याच्च कान्ति दहनप्रदीसिम्।
अशेषदोषोपचयं निहन्यादभ्यस्यमानं जलबस्तिकर्म॥ २८॥

(28)   This Basti when duly practiced, refines the bodily constitution, indriyas (sense organs), and the antahkarana (inner instrument). It makes the body bright and increases the digestive power. It destroys all the defects in the constitution.

सूत्रं वितस्ति सुस्निग्धं नासानाले प्रवेशयेत्।
मुखान्निर्गमयेच्चैषा   नेतिः सिद्धैर्निगद्यते॥ २९॥

(29) Draw up through one of the nostrils, a fine piece of [string] twelve fingers long, and draw it out through the mouth. This is Neti.

Brahmananda's Commentary: *The string should have no knots. The way to do this is to put one end of the string into the nose, and closing the other nostril with the finger, inhale and exhale through the mouth. By a repetition of this process, the string gets into the mouth. Then take it and pull it out. You can also pass the string through one nostril and draw it through the other.*

कपालशोधनी चैव दिव्यदृष्टिप्रदायिनी।
जत्रूर्ध्वजातरोगौघं नेतिराशु निहन्ति च॥ ३०॥

(30) This purifies the skull and makes the sight very keen. Also it removes the diseases in the parts above the shoulders.

निरीक्षेन्निश्चलदृशा सूक्ष्मलक्ष्यं समाहितः।
अश्रुसम्पातपर्यन्तमाचार्यैस्त्राटकं स्मृतम्॥ ३१॥

(31) Look (without winking the eyelids) at a minute object with your mind concentrated till the tears come into the eyes. This is called Trataka by the gurus.

मोचनं नेत्ररोगाणां तन्द्रादीनां कपाटकम्।
यत्नतस्त्राटकं गोप्यं यथा हाटकपेटकम्॥ ३२॥

(32) By Trataka, all the diseases of the the eye and sloth are removed. So it should be carefully preserved secretly as a golden casket.

अमन्दावर्तवेगेन   तुन्दं   सव्यापसव्यतः।
नतांसो भ्रामयेदेषा नौलिः सिद्धैः प्रचक्ष्यते॥ ३३॥

(33) With the head bent down, one should turn the intestines of the stomach to the right and left with the slow motion of a small eddy in the river. This is called Nauli by the siddhas.

मन्दाग्निसन्दीपनपाचनादिसन्धापिकानन्दकरी   सदैव।
अशेषदोषामयशोषणी च हठक्रियामौलिरियं च नौलिः॥ ३४॥

(34) This Nauli, the crown of Hatha Yoga practices, drives away the dullness of the gastric fire, increases the digestive power, produces a pleasing sensation and destroys all diseases and disorders of the humours.

भस्त्रावल्लोहकारस्य   रेचपूरौ ससंभ्रमौ।
कपालभातिर्विख्याता कफदोषविशोषणी॥ ३५॥

*(35) Perform rechaka and puraka rapidly like the
bellows of a blacksmith. This is called Kapalabhati,
and destroys diseases of the phlegm.*

षट्कर्मनिर्गतस्थौल्यकफदोषमलादिक: ।
प्राणायामं तत: कुर्यादनायासेन सिद्धयति ॥ ३६ ॥

*(36) One freed from corpulence and phlegm by the
performance of the above six acts succeeds very easily
if he begins to practice pranayama afterwards.*

प्राणायामैरेव सर्वे प्रशुष्यन्ति मला   इति ।
आचार्याणां तु केषाञ्चिदन्यत्कर्म न सम्मतम् ॥ ३७ ॥

*(37) Some teachers say that all the impurities (of
the nadis) are removed by pranayama only and not
by any other means.*

उदरगतपदार्थमुद्वमन्ति   पवनमपानमुदीर्य   कण्ठनाले।
क्रमपरिचयवश्यनाडिचक्रा गजकरणीति निगद्यते हठज्ञै: ॥ ३८ ॥

*(38) Contracting the anus, draw up the apana to
the throat and vomit the things that are in the
stomach. This act that gradually brings the nadi
chakras under control is called Gajakarani.*

ब्रह्मादयोऽपि त्रिदशा: पवनाभ्यासतत्परा: ।
अभूवन्नन्तकभयात्तस्मात्पवनमभ्यसेत् ॥ ३९ ॥

*(39) Brahma and gods, devoting themselves to the
practice of pranayama, were freed from the fear of
death. So one should practice it.*

When prana goes to the Sushumna there is no longer any fear at all.

यावद् बद्धो मरुद्देहे यावच्चित्तं निराकुलम् ।
यावद् दृष्टिर्भ्रुवोर्मध्ये तावत्कालभयं कुत: ॥ ४० ॥

*(40) So long as the breath is restrained, so long as
the mind is firm and steady, so long as the eye is
directed towards the middle of the eyebrows, why
should one fear death?*

By "breath restrained" is meant that the prana is in the Sushumna. A
mind "firm and steady" is a mind calm and steady. "The eye directed
towards the middle of the eyebrows" does not mean the physical eye
only, but also the mental eye.

विधिवत्प्राणसंयामैर्नाडीचक्रे विशोधिते ।
सुषुम्नावदनं भित्त्वा सुखाद्विशति मारुत: ॥ ४१ ॥

*(41) When the nadi chakras have been purified by a
regular course of pranayama, the breath easily forces
itself into the mouth of the Sushumna and enters it.*

At that time prana will go automatically.

मारुते मध्यसञ्चारे मन:स्थैर्य प्रजायते।
यो मन:सुस्थिरीभाव: सैवावस्था मनोन्मनी ॥ ४२ ॥

*(42) When the breath flows through the Sushumna,
then the mind becomes steady. This steadiness of
the mind is called Unmani avastha.*

Hatha Yoga Samadhi is called Unmani avastha.

तत्सिद्धये विधानज्ञाश्चित्रान् कुर्वन्ति कुम्भकान्।
विचित्रकुम्भकाभ्यासाद्विचित्रां सिद्धिमाप्नुयात् ॥ ४३ ॥

*(43) To attain it, the wise ones practice various
sorts of kumbhakas. By a practice of the various
kumbhakas one obtains various siddhis.*

Brahmananda's Commentary: *As said in the **Bhagavatam**,
one obtains, through the practice of Yoga, those siddhis that are
obtained severally by his previous karma, by plants, or by
religious austerities and mantras.*

सूर्यभेदनमुज्जायी सीत्कारी शीतली तथा।
भस्त्रिका भ्रामरी मूर्च्छा प्लाविनीत्यष्टकुम्भका: ॥ ४४ ॥

*(44) There are eight kumbhakas: Surya bheda,
Ujjayi, Sitkari, Sitali, Bhastrika, Brahmari, Moorcha,
and Plavini.*

पूरकान्ते तु कर्त्तव्यो बन्धो जालन्धराभिधः ।
कुम्भकान्ते रेचकादौ कर्त्तव्यस्तूड्डियानकः ॥ ४५ ॥

*(45)   At the end of the puraka [inhalation] or during
kumbhaka [retention], the Jalandhara bandha should
be practiced. At the end of kumbhaka and at the
beginning of rechaka he should practice Uddiyana
bandha.*

Jalandhara bandha will block up the prana at one of the most
important acupressure areas where various nerves come from. The
lungs and the cardiovascular system are both controlled by Jalandhara
at the throat. Mula bandha controls the anal sphincter muscles.
Jalandhara bandha is practiced as follows: the throat is contracted and
the chin firmly placed on the chest.

अधस्तात् कुञ्चनेनाशु कण्ठसङ्कोचने कृते ।
मध्ये पश्चिमतानेन स्यात् प्राणो ब्रह्मनाडिगः ॥ ४६ ॥

*(46)   Contracting the throat
[Jalandhara bandha] and the anus
[Mula bandha] at the same time,
the breath flows through the
Sushumna, being drawn in through
the back part of the navel.*

When both bandhas are applied, the prana flows through the
Sushumna for those who are purified through diet and all those things
we mentioned. Then prana flows through the Sushumna naturally; it
happens automatically without your having to do anything additional

about it. Jihva bandha is the tongue lock. If this lock is not known, the anal and chin locks can be practiced without it.

> **Brahmananda's Commentary:** *If one has learned from his guru the Jihva (tongue) bandha, by practicing this first and Jalandhara bandha afterwards, pranayama follows easily. But if the Jihva bandha is not known, then one should contract the anus [Mula bandha]. These three bandhas are to be learned from guru, for if practiced wrongly, they bring on various diseases.*

अपानमूर्ध्वमुत्थाप्य प्राणं कण्ठादधो नयेत्।
योगी जराविमुक्त: सन् षोडशाब्दवयो भवेत्॥ ४७॥

(47) Raising the apana upwards (by contracting the anus) and forcing the prana downwards from the throat, the yogi becomes a lad of sixteen, ever free from old age.

This is apana [downward moving prana]; here its impulse is pulled upward. To get a clear picture of apana, suppose you are driving along a highway and you want to go to the bathroom (your bladder is near to bursting), what do you do? You hold it until you find a toilet, and at that time your bladder is relieved. This control is Mula bandha.

In ancient times, advanced yogis practiced this through Vajroli mudra also (and I am not suggesting that you do it) when they drew water up through the urethra into the bladder with a catheter. It is just like Nauli. This is called "drawing back by the pull of the apana." At first they practiced with water, and then gradually they advanced to the use of milk and honey. Eventually they practiced this in the man-woman union: they could stop the outward flow of the seminal fluid and pull it backwards. Thus the apana for discharging the energy was stopped so that there was no feeling of ejaculation or depression after the sexual act. This tells us that if you know how to control the apana, you will automatically have natural control of moving the sexual energy upwards. This is not part of our practice, but you should have an idea about it.

Those who have difficulties with sexual control can practice Vajroli mudra. This mudra also happens automatically as you contract the anal sphincter muscle in the practice of Mula bandha and also in another mudra called Ashwini mudra, where you sit in water and contract and release the anal sphincter muscles. This practice will help people who have a lack of control such as premature ejaculation or other problems related to the sexual organs. They should, of course, practice this along with the regular practice of pranayama, bandhas and mudras. Then it will become a natural habit for them to draw the apana upwards automatically without any effort. It is a long practice, but like Basti, in time you get full control so that the impulse is withdrawn backwards. Then the the apana will not come outwards in the form of a sexual ejaculation.

Apana is used in all sexual acts, in excretion, and also during childbirth. It is apana which is the impulse pushing out the baby. Childbirth is painful because the impulses are coming in an extremely powerful way. A tremendous amount of energy is needed to get the baby out of the mother's womb.

> **Brahmananda's Commentary:** *In this the Mula bandha and the Jalandhara bandha are mentioned; Uddiyana bandha is not mentioned as it naturally follows from the above.*

Uddiyana bandha happens naturally when you exhale. In time, with practice, all three bandhas happen automatically.

आसने सुखदे योगी बद्ध्वा चैवासनं तत:।
दक्षनाड्या समाकृष्य बहि:स्थं पवनं शनै: ॥ ४८ ॥

(48) Placing himself on a convenient seat and assuming an easy asana, the yogi should slowly draw the breath through the right nadi, Pingala. This is Surya bheda.

Brahmananda's Commentary: *Here I shall quote from a work on Yoga a description of the daily life that a yogi is expected to lead:*

"He should get up at four or six o'clock in the morning. Having contemplated upon his guru in his mind and his duty in his heart, he should clean his teeth and besmear himself with holy ashes.

"Seated on a soft and convenient seat in a pleasant math, he should mentally salute his guru. Then he should perform sankalpa .... Afterwards he should make as many salutations as he can to Sesha, the king of the serpents, that he may safely go through the asanas. He should then practice the asanas, and when he gets fatigued, the Savasana. He should perform the practice called Viparita karani. Then, having performed achamana (sipping the water and pronouncing a mantra), he should salute the great yogis.

"He should then assume the Siddhasana and should perform ten pranayamas, increasing the number by five every day until he reaches eighty. He should first practice Kevala kumbhaka by the right and left nadis. Then follows Surya bheda, Ujjayi, Sitkari, Sitali, and Bhastrika, and then the others. Then the mudras should be practiced as taught by the guru. He should then assume the Padmasana posture and practice concentration upon the inner sounds. In the end he should offer up all these to Ishwara.

"Having got up, he should bathe in hot water. Then the daily duties should be performed very quickly. The same process should be gone through in the midday. After that he should take some rest and proceed to take his meals. Then he should take cloves, camphor, or betel leaf without chunam (lime). After the meal he should study the shastras that treat of emancipation, or he should hear the puranas expounded or repeat the names of Ishwara.

"When it is an hour and a half to sunset, he should begin to practice as before, and then perform the Sandhyavandana. He should not practice Viparita karani in the evening and midnight or after a meal. Then he should begin to practice at midnight."

आकेशादानखाग्राच्च निरोधावधि कुम्भयेत् ।
ततः शनैः सव्यनाड्या रेचयेत्पवनं शनैः ॥ ४९ ॥

(49) He should practice kumbhaka until he feels that prana pervades the whole of his body from the head to the toe. Then he should slowly exhale it through the left nostril.

कपालशोधनं वातदोषघ्नं कृमिदोषहृत् ।
पुनः पुनरिदं कार्यं सूर्यभेदनमुत्तमम् ॥ ५० ॥

(50) This Surya bedha kumbhaka should again and again be performed, as it purifies the brain and destroys diseases arising from the excess of wind and cures maladies caused by worms [bacteria, etc.].

Next is Ujjayi:

मुखं संयम्य नाडीभ्यामाकृष्य पवनं शनैः ।
यथा लगति कण्ठात्तु हृदयावधि सस्वनम् ॥ ५१ ॥

(51) Closing the mouth, draw up the breath through (both) the nostrils till the breath fills the space from throat to the heart with a noise.

पुर्ववत्कुम्भयेत्प्राणं रेचयेदिडया तथा:।
श्लेष्मदोषहरं कण्ठे देहानलविवर्धनम्॥ ५२॥

(52) Perform kumbhaka as before and exhale
through Ida (left). This removes disorders in the
throat caused by phlegm and stimulates the
[digestive] fire in the body.

नाडीजलोदराधातुगतदोषविनाशनम्।
गच्छता तिष्ठता कार्यमुज्जाय्याख्यं तु कुम्भकम्॥ ५३॥

(53) This is called Ujjayi, and it should be practiced
walking or sitting. It removes all diseases from the
nadis, and the dhatus, as also the dropsy.

The seven dhatus are: skin, flesh, blood, bones, marrow, fat, and semen.

सीत्कां कुर्यात्तथा वक्त्रे घ्राणेनैव विजृम्भिकाम्।
एवमभ्यासयोगेन   कामदेवो   द्वितीयक:॥ ५४॥

(54) Putting the tongue between the lips
and drawing the breath in the mouth with
a hissing sound, the puraka should be
made, and then the rechaka by the two
nostrils only (and not by the mouth).
This is called Sitkari. By repeating this he
becomes a second god of beauty.

Sitkari differs from Brahmari which has a sound like a bumblebee
(very hard). Ujjayi is very mild, very slight.　Ujjayi is a major
pranayama, while Brahmari, Sitali, and Sitkari are minor pranayamas.
A minor pranayama is one which is not very important, but is used for
special conditions.　For example: Sitali and Sitkari can be used on hot
days to cool off the body.　They can also be used when the blood is
impure or when you wish to stimulate the throat center; the latter is
the main purpose of Sitali and Sitkari.　Under hot and dry conditions
where you cannot get water, Sitali can be performed as a kind of
refrigeration by taking the cool, moist air to the psychic center which
creates that thirst.

योगिनीचक्रसंमान्यसृष्टिसंहारकारक: ।
न क्षुधा न तृषा निद्रा नैवालस्यं प्रजायते ॥ ५५ ॥

*(55) Among the multitude of women he becomes an
object of admiration;*

He [the author] is giving some kind of chocolate so that people will
practice.　What this really means is that when there is an abundance of
prana, everyone is attracted to your personality.　Naturally, when there is
honey, honeybees will come.　Here the attraction is not due to the body,
but to the prana.　When there is no prana, you are like a stale pizza.　When
you have lots of prana; like a beautiful fresh rose people are attracted.
Then, as you become older, due to excessive sexual acts, menstruation,
gastric problems, lactation, etc., much prana is lost, and then no-one
wants to touch you.　But if you practice pranayama, there is no old age
and so people are attracted to you all the time.

*he is able to do and undo; and feels neither hunger,
thirst, nor indolence.*

This means that if there is food, he will take it.　But if he cannot get
food at his regular time, he can just take a few deep breaths and stop
the hunger impulse.　He is not a slave of that particular habit.

भवेत्सत्त्वं च देहस्य सर्वोपद्रववर्जितः।
अनेन विधिना सत्यं योगोन्द्रो भूमिमण्डले ॥ ५६ ॥

*(56) By this practice he gains strength of body, and
becoming lord of the yogis, remains undoubtedly free
from afflictions of every kind on this earthly sphere.*

जिह्वया वायुमाकृष्य पूर्ववत्कुम्भ-साधनम्।
शनकैर्घ्राणरन्ध्राभ्यां रेचयेत्पवनं सुधीः॥ ५७ ॥

*(57) Protruding the tongue a little way from the
lips, inhale the prana and, having performed
kumbhaka, the intelligent practitioner should slowly
breathe out through the nostrils.*

गुल्मप्लीहादिकान् रोगाञ्ज्वरं पित्तं क्षुधां तृषाम्।
विषाणि शीतली नाम कुम्भिकेयं निहन्ति हि ॥ ५८ ॥

*(58) This kumbhaka called Sitali,
destroys diseases of the abdomen and
spleen and other diseases, as also fever,
bilious complaints, hunger, thirst, and
the bad effects of poisons, i.e.
snakebites, etc.*

ऊर्वोरुपरि संस्थाप्य शुभे पादतले उभे।
पद्मासनं भवेदेतत्सर्वपापप्रणाशनम् ॥ ५९ ॥

*(59) Now Bhastrika is described: Place the feet upon
the opposite thighs. This is called Padmasana and it
destroys all diseases.*

सम्यक्पद्मासनं बद्ध्वा समग्रीवोदरं सुधी:।
मुखं संयम्य यत्नेन प्राणं घ्राणेन रेचयेत् ॥ ६० ॥

*(60) Assuming this posture, he should close the
mouth and breathe out through his nostrils until the
pressure is felt on the heart, the throat and the brain.*

यथा लगति हृत्कण्ठे कपालावधि सस्वनम्।
वेगेन पूरयेच्चापि हृत्पद्मावधि मारुतम् ॥ ६१ ॥

*(6l) Then he should draw in the breath rapidly with
a hissing sound till it strikes against the heart, all
this time keeping his body and head erect.*

पुनर्विरेचयेत्तद्वत्पूरयेच्च पुन: पुन:।
यथैव लोहकारेण भस्त्रा वेगेन चाल्यते ॥ ६२ ॥

*(62) Again, he should draw in the breath and exhale
it as before directed. Go on, again and again, as the
blacksmith works his bellows rapidly.*

This is Bhastrika, which means bellows. You continue like a blacksmith working his bellows until the prana goes to all the chakras. Only if the nadis are first purified from alternate nostril breathing will Bhastrika bring any benefit.

Surya bheda and Ujjayi are heating because they use the right nostril; Sitkari and Sitali are cold. So on hot days you practice Sitali and Sitkari instead of Bhastrika. For the practice of Surya bedha and Ujjayi, you must be in a cool place. Bhastrika uses both nostrils equally, and so is energy-balanced on both sides of the Sushumna. On very hot days, you should omit the practice of Bhastrika during midday; you must be in a cool place for Bhastrika.

तथैव स्वशरीरस्थं चालयेत्पवनं धिया।
यदा श्रमो भवेद्देहे तदा सूर्येण पूरयेत्॥ ६३ ॥

(63) He should then keep the prana constantly moving (by rechaka and puraka) in his body. When he gets tired, he should breathe in by the right nostril.

यथोदरं भवेत्पूर्णमनिलेन तथा लघु।
धारयेन्नासिकां मध्यातर्जनीभ्यां विना दृढम्॥ ६४ ॥

(64) When the breath rapidly fills the interior of the body, he should close his nose by the thumb, the ring and the little fingers.

विधिवत्कुम्भकं कृत्वा रेचयेदिडयानिलम्।
वातपित्तश्लेष्महरं   शरीराग्निविवर्धनम्॥ ६५ ॥

(65) *Having performed kumbhaka according to the rules, he should breathe out through the left nostril. This removes the diseases arising from the excess of wind, bile, and phlegm, and increases the digestive fire in the body.*

Brahmananda's Commentary: *Bhastrika kumbhaka should be thus performed: press the left nostril with the ring and the little fingers, and with the right nostril inhale and exhale as a bellows. If he feels tired, he should perform kumbhaka, inhaling by the right nostril and exhaling by the left nostril. Then he should press the nostrils, and by the right nostril he should inhale and exhale like a bellows. He should go on alternately till he feels tired. This is one method.*

Another way of practicing is to close the left nostril and inhale as much as possible by the right nostril, then exhaling gradually by the left nostril. This should be done several times, and if he should then feel tired, he should perform kumbhaka and exhale through the Ida Nadi.

कुण्डलीबोधकं क्षिप्रं पवनं सुखदं हितम् ।
ब्रह्मनाडीमुखे   संस्थकफाद्यर्गलनाशनम् ॥ ६६ ॥

(66) *This rouses the Kundalini quickly. It purifies the nadis considerably, it is pleasant and is the most beneficial of all the kumbhakas. It removes the phlegm that is at the mouth of Sushumna.*

Brahmananda's Commentary: *Surya bheda and Ujjayi generate heat; Sitkari and Sitali are both cool. Bhastrika preserves equal temperature. Again, Surya bheda destroys the excess of wind. Ujjayi destroys phlegm. Sitkari and Sitali destroy bile. Bhastrika [destroys] all three.*

सम्यग्गात्रसमुद्भूत   ग्रन्थित्रयविभेदकम्।
विशेषेणैव कर्त्तव्यं भस्त्राख्यं कुम्भकं त्विदम्॥ ६७॥

(67) This Bhastrika kumbhaka should be specially practiced, as it enables the breath to break through the three granthis, or knots, that are firmly placed in the Sushumna.

You cannot break all the granthis at one time. First there is the Brahma granthi of the Muladhara chakra. When the prana and apana unite and the Kundalini awakens, it is this granthi which is broken. Then, as years go by, the prana goes up to the Manipura chakra where the second granthi, the Vishnu granthi exists. The breaking of this granthi is very difficult, so several lifetimes may be required to break it. The last granthi is the Rudra granthi at the Ajna chakra; when it is broken, the prana goes to the Sahasrara chakra. Bhastrika pranayama breaks these three granthis after purification has taken place, and it is only through Bhastrika that you can break the granthis.

वेगाद् घोषं पूरकं भृङ्गनादं भृङ्गीनादं रेचकं मन्दमन्दम्।
योगीन्द्राणामेवमभ्यासयोगाच्चित्ते जाता काचिदानन्दलीला॥ ६८॥

(68) Fill in the air rapidly, making the sound of a male bee, and again exhale it, making the sound of a female bee humming. (Practice kumbhaka). The great yogis by a constant practice of this, feel an indescribable joy in their hearts. This is Brahmari.

पूरकान्ते गाढतरं बद्ध्वा जालन्धरं शनै:।
रेचयेन्मूर्च्छनाख्येयं मनोमूर्च्छा सुखप्रदा॥ ६९॥

(69) At the end of the puraka, practice the
Jalandhara bandha and exhale the breath slowly.
This is Moorcha kumbhaka, as it reduces mind to a
state of inactivity and gives pleasure.

अन्तःप्रवर्त्तितोदारमारुता – पूरितोदरः।
पयस्यगाधेऽपि सुखात् प्लवते पद्मपत्रवत्॥ ७० ॥

(70) Having filled the lungs completely with the air
till they are distended, the yogi moves upon waters of
great depth like a lotus leaf. This is Plavini.

प्राणायामस्त्रिधा प्रोक्तो रेचपूरककुम्भकैः।
सहितः केवलश्चेति कुम्भको द्विविधो मतः ॥ ७१ ॥

(71) There are three kinds of pranayama: rechaka,
puraka, and kumbhaka. Kumbhaka is also of two
kinds: Sahita and Kevala.

Brahmananda's Commentary: *The first kind of pranayama
consists in performing rechaka first, i.e. exhaling and stopping
inhalation; the second in doing puraka first, i.e. inhaling and
retaining the breath inside, thus filling the nadis; the third
consists in inhaling and holding the air as in a pot. (This is the
same as the second pranayama.) Another type of Kumbhaka
consists in stopping the breath, i.e. being without Puraka and
Recaka. The Sahita kumbhaka is of two sorts: the first type is
preceded by Recaka and resembles the first kind of Pranayama,
the second type is preceded by Puraka and resembles the second
kind of pranayama. Kevala kumbhaka is the same as
Kumbhaka pranayama.*

यावत्केवलसिद्धि: स्यात् सहितं तावदभ्यसेत्।
रेचकं पूरकं मुक्त्वा सुखं यद्वायुधारणम् ॥ ७२ ॥

(72) As long as one does not achieve Kevala kumbhaka (which consists in restraining the breath without puraka and rechaka), he should practice Sahita.

Sahita kumbhaka is the retention of the regular pranayama with controlled inhalation and exhalation.

For how many years will you continue to practice pranayama? Until you reach Kevala kumbhaka. Kevala kumbhaka is the automatic suspension of breath which occurs when both the right and left nostrils come into balance. Eventually this becomes a natural thing, so that when you sit for meditation the breath stops – just now and then there is an occasional very slow breath through both nostrils. When Kevala kumbhaka is attained, then you can discontinue your practice of pranayama. It takes a long time to attain, but if you continue your practice over the years, it happens. It is similar to the slowing down or stoppage of breath when you are trying to hear something.

When the prana goes in the Sushumna, you can hear the inner sound or feel the peaceful state. When you attain that, you don't have to continue the intense asanas and pranayama practice – three or four hours of asanas, pranayama, bandhas, mudras, etc. are no longer necessary. Just continue with a few asanas and pranayama so that the body will be healthy and the diaphragm will continue to move in the right direction. At that time you should practice every day only ten or twenty rounds of alternate nostril breathing, omitting Bhastrika and the other pranayamas. Then you should try more to hear the inner sound and to keep the prana in the Sushumna through concentration.

Brahmananda's Commentary: *The Sahita should be practiced until the prana enters Sushumna. This is known by a peculiar sound being produced in the Sushumna. Then he should practice only ten or twenty-five sahita kumbhakas and increase the Kevala kumbhakas to eighty.*

प्राणायामोऽयमित्युक्त: स वै केवलकुम्भक:।
कुम्भके केवले सिद्धे रेचपूरकवर्जिते ॥ ७३ ॥

न तस्य दुर्लभं किञ्चित् त्रिषु लोकेषु विद्यते।
शक्त: केवलकुम्भेन यथेष्टं वायुधारणात् ॥ ७४ ॥

राजयोगपदं चापि लभते नात्र संशय:।
कुम्भकात् कुण्डलीबोध: कुण्डलीबोधतो भवेत् ॥ ७५ ॥

*(73-75) This sort of pranayama is called Kevala
kumbhaka. When this kumbhaka has been mastered
without any rechaka or puraka, there is nothing
unattainable by him in the three worlds. He can
restrain his breath as long as he likes through this
kumbhaka. [Then] he obtains the stage of Raja Yoga.*

This is called "Chitta vritti nirodha."

Through this kumbhaka, the Kundalini is roused, and when it is so
roused, the Sushumna is free of all obstacles and he has attained
perfection in Hatha Yoga.

Perfection in Hatha Yoga is perfection in Raja Yoga; they are one and
the same.

अनर्गला सुषुम्ना च हठसिद्धिश्च जायते।
हठं विना राजयोगो राजयोगं विना हठ:।
न सिध्यति ततो युग्ममानिष्पत्ते: समभ्यसेत् ॥ ७६ ॥

*(76)   One cannot obtain perfection in Raja Yoga
without Hatha Yoga and vice versa, so he should
practice both till he attains perfection in Raja Yoga.*

This emphasizes the point that one should practice both Yogas
simultaneously: asanas and pranayama along with meditation and
mantras, not just one Yoga alone.

कुम्भकप्राणरोधान्ते कुर्याच्चित्तं निराश्रयम्।
एवमभ्यासयोगेन   राजयोगपदं   व्रजेत्॥ ७७॥

*(77)   At the end of the kumbhaka, he should draw
off his mind from any and every object whatever.*

That means pratyahara – don't let the senses go outward.

*By thus practicing regularly, he attains the stage of
Raja Yoga.*

वपुः कृशत्वं वदने प्रसन्नता नादस्फुटत्वं नयने सुनिर्मले।
अरोगता बिन्दुजयोऽग्निदीपनं नाडीविशुद्धिर्हठयोगलक्षणम्॥ ७८॥

(78)   The signs of perfection in Hatha Yoga are:

Indicating control of your prana and mind.

the body becomes lean, the speech eloquent,

Although you might not speak grammatically, still your speech is
very powerful.

the inner sounds are distinctly heard,

Or light may come very clearly.

the eyes are clear and bright, the body is freed from all diseases, the seminal fluid is concentrated,

That means that the seminal fluid will not go downward to the sexual organ. Automatically every day it goes backward unless you really want to bring it down.

the digestive fire is increased,

Your digestion becomes very good.

and the nadis are purified.

हठयोगप्रदीपिका

hatha yoga pradipika

CHAPTER THREE
INTRODUCTION
AWAKENING KUNDALINI

Kundalini is glorified by all. She Herself, when awakened by the Yogi, achieves illumination for him. It is she who bestows liberation and knowledge, for She is That Herself. She is the source of all knowledge and bliss. She is pure Consciousness Itself. She is Brahman, She is Prana Shakti, the Supreme Force, the Mother of Prana, fire, sound, and the source of all things.

–Swami Sivananda

CHAPTER THREE
INTRODUCTION

AWAKENING KUNDALINI

Since most people are content to live only in the lower chakras, their experience of this world is confined to the gross. For example, they may go out to eat in an expensive candle-lit restaurant. Their food is brought by waiters robed in white, carrying elegant covered silver platters. What do they get but the same dog food? (They call it steak.) They sit with a fork and a knife and cut it neatly this way and then put it that way. After eating, they may go to sleep or perhaps go out for a little dancing in order to prepare for a sexual experience later. The next morning they get up just to make money so that they can get power and position to continue this process. They cannot meditate or cogitate: "Who am I? Where do I come from? Where do I go?" One becomes a human being only when these questions begin to be asked, and this happens only when the Kundalini has awakened. Till then, the intellect is used only for the getting of food, sleep, and sensual enjoyments.

Awakening of the Kundalini means that your vibratory level goes up. At that time sensual experience becomes dull and boring; you no longer need drinking, smoking, gambling. It makes no sense to you because you have discovered that satisfaction, peace and happiness are within. Your peace and joy will increase proportionately as this is realized. What ordinary people consider as happiness, is for you nothing but pain. When that experience comes, it means that Kundalini has awakened.

Once the Kundalini is awakened, the fear of death also slowly disappears. Now you know that there is no birth, no death. You find disease vanishing automatically. This is because disease is caused by gross vibrations, by believing that you get happiness from the vibrations of these lower senses. These things will disappear automatically when the Kundalini is awakened.

But don't look for a serpent to come up and hit you. Don't think: "Oh, my Kundalini has reached the third chakra – the fourth chakra – now it is only two more inches to the fifth chakra." That's not the way the Kundalini gets awakened. In actuality, it is the aura condition that changes as the vibratory rate increases.

The highest stage, called God Consciousness, is where the Shakti vibrates with Siva. The lowest stage of Shakti is the experience we get in association with matter. Matter is gross. For example, when your senses come in contact with ice cream, you get an experience of Shakti; it vibrates at a very low level. All of our five senses are Shakti, but they vibrate only when they come in contact with objects, with matter.

When you eat, when you hear music, or when you see something, it excites the Shakti in a very low form. In our lives we are always having such experiences, but we are not happy about them. We want to increase that experience on a different wavelength. So we sit in meditation and try to: (1) quiet the thoughts, (2) regulate the breath, (3) shut off the five organs of action (mouth/speech, legs, hands, genitals and anus), and the five senses of knowledge (hearing, taste, smell, sight and touch). We get knowledge of the universe only through these five senses and we perform actions through the five organs of action. These ten faculties of man are called Indriyas in Sanskrit.

To make the Kundalini Shakti vibrate at a higher level, you must withdraw from contact with external objects. To awaken the Shakti, you must stop the energy from going to the ten faculties so that the mind becomes as still as possible. Then the senses are not reacting on the mind. The mind is not allowed to wander into sensual pathways. Each sense will say, "Come on, let me taste; let me hear," and will draw the mind to the sense objects. But once you are able to stop this extroverted, outward going tendency, you make the mind introverted.

When the mind becomes introverted and still, then the Shakti starts vibrating on a different wavelength. It is awakening to power in a higher state. When the Shakti vibrates only on lower levels, then you get only the five basic sensual experiences mentioned above – very crude and gross. There is a dissatisfaction with that experience.

You may remember how you used to go for holidays to a five-star hotel. Early morning you drank coffee, you smoked, you ate your breakfast with bacon and eggs, and then swallowed a couple of aspirins or pep pills. Afterwards you sat by the swimming pool or went to the golf course or went fishing. In the evening you ate your steak and then you went dancing. The senses went only in this direction; you never knew anything beyond that. But now you are looking for something else because you are unhappy living at the low energy level like that of an animal. You want to get out of the animal experience to a divine experience.

The ordinary human experience is very close to animal experience and perhaps even worse, because we become very clever at using the intellect to satisfy the senses: how to alter the natural flavor of food by cooking and spicing so that it will taste better, or how to combine it with certain drinks so that it will be even more tasty. In this way you use the intellect to prepare food, spending hours and hours in changing its nature so that it will have a different flavor and appearance. All the senses are brought into action – that is why there is unhappiness and pain in all of us. That pain has brought you to this point.

But by Raja Yoga we are stopping the outgoing senses and stilling the mind. Raja Yoga is called "Citta vritti nirodha," stopping the mental waves. In Hatha Yoga we stop the pranic waves so that the mental waves will stop. In Kundalini Yoga they say that when the senses are brought together, the energy will not move outward. At that time, thought will be in a higher vibratory level; the energy field will change. Actually, all these experiences are one and the same, only the point of view is different. There is really no difference between Kundalini Yoga, Hatha Yoga, Mantra Yoga, Laya Yoga, and Raja Yoga. Each Yoga may emphasize certain points, but they are not basically different from each other. They are all part of Ashtanga Yoga (the eight-limbed Yoga): yama, niyama, asana, pranayama, pratyahara, dharana, dhyana, and samadhi.

Mantra Yoga achieves energy/thought control by the use of mystic syllables. When you repeat "Om Namo Narayanaya" over and over again, you are changing the vibratory level of your thought. In

Kundalini Yoga, by pulling the energy upward through control of the prana, the energy field changes its wavelength. In Hatha Yoga, by controlling the prana, the Kundalini is pushed upward, and in this way too the energy level is changed. So you may say that eventually all these techniques are nothing but Kundalini Yoga. The Shakti must be controlled and transformed into a higher vibratory state.

When you perform asanas, you are not just performing physical exercise. Asanas also act on the psychic system (just as acupuncture affects the various meridians) by stimulating the prana. For example, when there is a problem in the liver, acupuncturists stimulate the appropriate area of a meridian with a needle so that the electrical impulses increase and the liver gets additional prana for its healing. But yogis can do the same without the need for needles, just from the asanas themselves. Take a Kirilian photograph before you do asanas and another one afterwards. You will see that the energy level has changed completely with a tremendous new emanation of energy. This has been proven by recent scientific research.

And when you perform pranayama, not only do you get oxygen, but the wavelength of the chakras (the energy field) changes. This is being investigated by Eastern as well as Western scientists. In Japan, researchers have a chakra machine which can actually measure the energy wavelength in each chakra. It is like an especially sensitive microphone which picks up the wavelength radiating from each chakra without even touching the body. The signal is then passed through an amplifier and into an oscilloscope so that the wave pattern can be viewed. Each chakra will be seen to show a different wave pattern. When advanced yogis meditate, their chakras vibrate rapidly and so the pattern in the oscilloscope changes. Before this recent research, we had no way to prove the existence of these human energy fields.

This shows that Kundalini Shakti is manifesting in a higher dimension. The purpose of all this pranayama is to increase the vibratory level or awaken the Kundalini Shakti – they are one and the same. That is why we use various methods: physical, mental and pranic. The physical method is by controlling the sphincter muscle of the anus, by applying Jalandhara bandha to affect the vagus nerve. When both impulses are controlled, the energy builds up.

It is like the electronic flash on a camera. When you turn on the flash, energy from the six-volt battery builds up in the condenser little by little. Then when you press the button, a flash of light comes (about 10,000 – 20,000 volts for a fraction of a second) to take the photograph. This flash is very intense and powerful, so you get a tremendous amount of light, even though for only a fraction of a second. The same thing happens when you hold the breath and control the energy.

As you hold the breath, your lower batteries start charging up – with both prana and apana. Then suddenly, one day when the nadis are purified, the energy starts flashing through the spinal cord in an instant. At that time all of the chakras are opened up. This is the awakening of the chakras by the movement of the Kundalini to the upper chakras. When you follow a practice of bandhas, mudras, asanas, pranayama, and purification by chanting mantras and eating the right diet – the energy must go up automatically. Your spiritual progress will increase proportionally as the energy level goes to the higher chakras. That is what is meant by the "awakening of the Kundalini Shakti."

This should be understood theoretically. The energy is within you; it is to be awakened. Do not make it grosser or bring it to a lower state. Withdraw the senses as much as you can and bring that energy to the higher centers through your imagination and concentration. Wherever you think, there the prana goes; that is a law. Conversely, wherever prana goes, there thought goes. Thought and prana are interrelated; one cannot move without the other also moving.

That is why concentration, imagination, and physical exercise together give you a complete holistic approach to the awakening of the Shakti. That is why you need asanas, pranayama, bandhas, mudras, right diet, and the right atmosphere. A right atmosphere would be beautiful mountains where the magnetic current (the prana) is very strong from all the vegetation. Everything in nature radiates so that you can absorb and store this prana for your higher spiritual development.

PRANA AS ELECTRICITY

Your physical body is like a machine. It runs on two types of energy: chemical energy, which comes from food, and psychic energy (called prana) which comes from all the objects we take in: food, water, air, and sunlight. These are the basic sources of our prana, and they are found everywhere in nature. Prana also exists in the vacuum of space, underground, and even in water. But it is not a chemical thing, it is electrical in nature. Your body is a storehouse of prana, and the blood system [circulatory system] acts as a transformer, diverting the prana from the astral to the physical.

Yogis do not believe that the body exists merely because of its physicochemical nature; to them it is basically electrical in nature. When the electrical connection from the astral to the physical is severed (like a battery disconnected from an engine), it doesn't matter how powerful the engine is, it cannot start. The impulses of prana travel through the astral to the physical through an astral umbilical cord at our solar plexus. When this cord is severed, no more prana can come to the physical body. If the prana comes in very small amounts then the body will be comatose (unconscious).

If you understand the electrical nature of our bodies, you will understand the purpose of pranayama. I will try to explain in modern terms, as some of the ancient terms are very difficult to grasp.

It is said that you can block the air in the Sushumna, in the throat region, in the stomach region, in the back region, in the ear region, in the eye region. Actually, how can you block the air in these places when the air which you inhale does not go into these places at all? What does this mean?

Actually, it is not a physical blockage, it is the diversion of energy from one source to another. In Yoga we call this energy "prana." The problem is that there is no English equivalent for this word, so it gets translated as "air." Even Indian yogis make this mistake when they don't know how to translate from the Sanskrit.

I like to explain these ideas using analogies with electronic terms. Most of you are familiar with such gadgets as radios, cameras, computers. There are three basic components common to all of them.

Similar things exist in your body, but please don't take what I say literally; it is only to help you to understand how such things as locks work in the body mechanism. When you do pranayama, it will help you a great deal if you understand this. Three things should be understood: (1) transformers, (2) condensers, and (3) resistors.

(1) **Transformers:** In electronic components there is always a source of power, usually a battery or household current. A small tape recorder cannot handle the 110 volt current as it enters the house, so it must be stepped down to a lower voltage by a transformer, otherwise the components will burn up. (There are step-down transformers and step-up transformers for decreasing and increasing the voltage.)

(2) **Condensers** (also called **Capacitors**) are storehouses of electricity. An example is the electronic flash in your camera. The electricity for the flash may come from a six volt battery, but that voltage cannot give enough light to take a photograph. What is needed is several thousand volts to create an intense light. So the energy coming from this small battery is stored up (it is not stepped up or stepped down) like a reservoir and accumulated till it can create a powerful flash for a brief moment.

(3) **Resistors:** Another concept in electronics that we should understand is that of resistance. We can increase or decrease the resistance to the flow of energy. More impurities will reduce the electrical flow. An example is the ordinary garden hose through which water flows at a specific velocity unless constricted by squeezing. The pump continues to try to force 16 gallons of water per minute through the hose, but when its capacity is reduced by constriction, the pressure goes up, and so the water comes out more forcefully.

In our body, something similar to a condenser also exists. Prana is like electricity but very subtle. All electricity flows through wires, and in our body it flows through nadis (or meridians in the Chinese system). The problem here, is that when I say nerve, many people understand only the visible type of nerve. The nadi is equivalent to the nerve in the physical body, but it may be called an astral nerve tube, as it exists not in the physical, but in the astral body. I will not be able to completely communicate this subject in electronic terms, but there does exist a similarity between a physical nerve and your astral nerve; they are counterparts. The difference is that one is visible and the other is not.

In our bodies, the impulse coming from the brain through the vagus nerve which controls the heart and lungs are all impulses called prana. Previously it was thought that the heart was not susceptible to voluntary control, that you could not control the heartbeat by concentration. But yogis can demonstrate that the heartbeat can be slowed down with concentration or by such practices as Jalandhara bandha. They shut down the flow of prana. We are not talking about physical prana, but psychic prana.

Thought can change your breathing rhythm as well as your heartbeat. Two important components of the body are together called the cardiovascular system because they are interdependent. When the body needs extra oxygen, the heart rate goes up. In order to make the lungs pump faster you have to stimulate the muscles of the diaphragm and intercostal muscles. That is done by the brain. In an emergency, say you are running because a tiger is chasing you and you are close to exhaustion, the adrenal glands will throw out adrenaline to give the heart an extra boost so that the lungs can breathe a bit faster for a short time. That's equivalent to the capacitor in electronic gadgets which I mentioned. Nature has given us this ability to escape from dangerous situations. This extra stimulation activates the adrenal gland which pumps adrenaline into the blood stream so that the heart gets a fast kick for a short time so that it can pump more oxygen to the muscles. Let us try to understand the cardiovascular system, to see how the heart rate and the breathing are interconnected.

There is a gadget called the polygraph or lie detector. Just as EEG tests the brain waves, the polygraph measures the three basic components mostly connected to the autonomous nervous system, a system which is basically not under our control. Generally speaking, the autonomous nervous system is beyond our control, but yogis can control it. In the polygraph, the three basic components are: (1) to demonstrate and measure your breathing pattern, how many cycles per second you are breathing (normally we breathe 16 times per minute); (2) the pulse rate (normally about 75 or 80 per minute); (3) galvanic skin response. Under our sweat glands there are nerves which carry sensory impulses.

Because the galvanic skin response (GSR), measured as coming from the sweat gland, will change according to your thought, it is one of the three basic components in a polygraph. When you check for GSR by putting small electrodes on the tip of the finger (for example), you can take this current coming out and amplify it so that you can see its pattern. That is also under the autonomous nervous system.

The polygraph technician also connects an elastic type of material from your chest to the polygraph so that you can see the number of times you are breathing, or what your breathing pattern is: shallow, long, or disturbed. With normal breathing we inhale about 1500 cc of air and exhale out the same amount very gently. But when you are breathing deeply, you can take in and out about 2000 cc. At that time the impulse will be very strong. When you are mentally disturbed the breathing pattern will also change.

When all these components are connected to the polygraph, we observe three different waves: breathing pattern, blood pressure, and galvanic skin resistance. After two or three minutes there is a normal reading. If suddenly the polygraph changes, it is an indication that the person has lied. An emotional upset will cause the breathing pattern to change from say sixteen times per minute to twenty-five or thirty times per minute. It can go up or down. In extreme cases the breathing or the heart may even stop, as in the case of shock or some bad news. Also good news: something very exciting – say you won five million dollars in a lottery – that could stop the heart also.

In such cases you are overloading your capacitor. Within a brief time, everything is short circuited. The voltage coming through the nerves becomes so powerful that it just short circuits everything: the heart and/or lungs stop and there is collapse. So you see that your body is not different from an electronic mechanism.

The electronic impulse in our body is the prana. This prana comes to the nervous system where it is stored by condensers and transformed by transformers. There are five basic types of prana: prana, apana, udana, samana, and vyana, as well as some minor pranas; the difference between major and minor pranas lying in the voltage. Even in electronic gadgets, some things need higher voltage so there are different types of transformers. [In the body] we call these transformers chakras. Various nerves come and go through the chakras. They are not physical nerves, but astral.

In the physical body, the places where these nerves gather at the spinal cord are called plexuses. They are a kind of junction like a telephone exchange. These plexuses correspond to the chakras. This is where the energy is stored up like a condenser, altered like a transformer and acted upon by resistors. All these things take place in the same area.

In most people, the transformers in their upper chakras are not completely opened up; maybe for highly advanced students they are partially opened. Or if there is a tremendous amount of impurity, it acts as a resistor. These variable resistors are automatically controlled by your thought [as well as your diet]. Everything is controlled by thought. According to the nature of your thought, your impurities will increase or decrease. For each of these three gadgets in your system: condenser, transformer, resistor, all are controlled by your mind.

So yogis go directly to the mind to change the pattern. According to the nature of the'pattern of your thought, the voltage will be increased or reduced. If the voltage increases, then the energy goes to a higher chakra. If you reduce the voltage (make your thought very gross with only sensual and sexual thoughts), then the energy goes only to the lower chakras because the voltage is not sufficient to lift to the higher chakras.

Remember that neither thought nor prana are in the physical body. They are in the astral body and according to the nature of your thought, the prana flows in the physical body. When your thought is very gross, then the prana or electrons coming to the physical body will be lessened since there is too much resistance. Also, a physical nerve cannot take a high, powerful thought, so there may be a shutdown of the prana to a certain extent. The nervous system which is impure cannot transmit high voltage. Sometimes a sudden shock to the mind will even shut off this flow of prana. Sometimes this current is slowed down to such an extent that you are like a living corpse. Then you are in a coma.

BANDHAS AND MUDRAS

Bandhas are locks; they lock the prana in a certain area. Mudras are seals; they seal certain things and cause the energy to flow in only one direction instead of alternately. Again, we have to go back to electronics to understand these things.

You all now understand about resistance. Another thing to consider is alternating current (AC) and direct current (DC). The light bulbs in our homes work off alternating current because the positive and negative poles change as the dynamo rotates. On the other hand, direct current (DC), such as the current from a battery will light such gadgets as a flashlight. With DC, the flow of electrons is not alternating; it comes in steady streams.

When we apply the seals (mudras) and locks (bandhas), we are allowing the electrons to flow in only one direction (not alternately), and we are stopping the afferent and efferent currents (the motor and sensory impulses). In this way, the normal pattern of energy throughout the nervous system is altered. Through bandhas, mudras and pranayama, we control the sensory and motor nerves.

If you regularly practice the above (with purification of the nadis), then the energy will flow through one channel, the Sushumna, like direct current. This gives a high voltage, less resistance and more capacitance. When you have all these put together in an electronic component such as the electronic flash, the capacitor is charged and voltage builds up until there is an intense discharge of bright light for a fraction of a second. Too much resistance will cause everything to blow up because the flow through that wire must be sufficient to accommodate all those electrons. So we must remember the concepts of resistance, a build-up of voltage, and eventual discharge.

This also happens in our sexual experience. The capacitors are charged from thoughts and passion, and then in the sexual climax, suddenly there is a discharge of the prana. Afterwards there is no energy for you. You all know how the sexual act (or any strong emotion such as anger) literally drains the body of energy. After discharge takes place, it takes several hours to recharge the capacitors. It is just like an electrical flash: you can't press the discharge button immediately and get light again, you have to wait to build up the charge once more. That is why after the sexual act you have to wait for the body to recharge. A man who goes on wasting this energy, one day will become impotent like a dead battery. Then there is no happiness in him, no peace of mind. It's not just physical impotence I'm talking about – there will also be mental impotence. Thought becomes dull; one becomes unable to properly channel thought currents, and emotional complications take place, resulting in constant depression. All of this happens due to excessive discharge of prana.

Western scientists do not properly understand this. They think that the sexual act is a natural thing. It is not. It needs a tremendous amount of charging of the capacitors, and then there is release of that energy in a very short time. Suppose you were to continually discharge the flash on your camera after each build up of the capacitor, soon the battery would become so completely discharged that you would have to replace it. However, in our bodies we cannot change the battery; we have to wait while we recharge normally or do pranayama. Ordinary people do not know what pranayama is, so they can recharge only through rest, sunshine and eating food. You get some prana from eating food, but it is a very little bit: just the minimum amount for survival and the carrying on of vegetative functions.

Ordinary people cannot do higher practices of meditation, thinking, higher willing. Even though they may be doctors, psychiatrists, PhDs, they don't even have enough willpower to stop their smoking habits as their higher psychic capacities are very limited. They are continuously discharging and they don't know how to recharge. Their mind is in a very weak condition. If you understand this, then you understand the purpose of bandhas and mudras.

From practicing pranayama along with the bandhas and mudras, you are slowly channelling the current into one direction. Normally your energy is oscillating, like alternating current. As you channel the energy into one current, your capacitors charge up. Each time you hold the breath, you are recharging the capacitors. As each chakra transformer pulsates, the voltage increases and goes to higher and higher chakras. As the voltage goes up, each chakra acts like a step-up transformer, increasing the energy level step by step until the energy reaches the Sahasrara. That is called union.

This is the theory behind Kundalini Yoga. In philosophical terms, the aim of spiritual practice is freedom from mundane life into divine life. In Kundalini terms, this freedom or Mumukshutva is actually an escape from the lower voltage to a higher voltage.

CHAPTER THREE

सशैलवनधात्रीणां   यथाधारोऽहिनायकः ।
सर्वेषां योगतन्त्राणां तथाधारो हि कुण्डली ॥ १ ॥

*(1) As Ananta, the Lord of Serpents, supports this
whole universe with its mountains and forests, so
Kundalini is the main support of all the Yoga practices.*

सुप्ता गुरुप्रसादेन यदा जागर्ति कुण्डली ।
तदा सर्वाणि पद्मानि भिद्यन्ते ग्रन्थयोऽपि च ॥ २ ॥

*(2) When the sleeping Kundalini is aroused by the
grace of the guru, then all the lotuses (the chakras or
mystic nerve centers) and granthis (knots) are pierced.*

The granthis are in the Sushumna. The Brahma Granthi is in the
Muladhara Chakra, the Vishnu Granthi in the Manipura Chakra, the
Rudra Granthi in the Ajna Chakra. They can be broken by practicing
pranayama, bandhas and mudras.

What is meant by "the grace of the guru?" If you have faith in the guru,
he will teach you when you are ready to practice.

प्राणस्य शून्यपदवी तथा   राजपथायते ।
तदा चित्तं निरालम्बं तदा कालस्य वञ्चनम् ॥ ३ ॥

(3) Then Sushumna becomes the royal road for Prana. The mind remains suspended and the yogi cheats death.

सुषुम्ना शून्यपदवी ब्रह्मरन्ध्रं महापथ:।
श्मशानं शाम्भवी मध्यमार्गश्चेत्येकवाचका: ॥ ४ ॥

(4) Sushumna, Sunyapadavi (the great void), Brahmarandhra (the entry to Brahman), Mahapatha (the great road), Smasana (the burning ground), Shambhavi (pertaining to the auspicious Shambu), and Madhyamarga (the middle path), all refer to the same thing.

This is difficult to understand, though if you are practicing you will understand a little bit. "The void" is a literal translation from the Sanskrit "shunya," meaning no quality, no time or space or awareness. So, when the prana goes into the Sushumna, the world becomes non-existent. Time awareness, space awareness, experiences of the senses are only created by the mind, by thought. Ordinarily, sometimes you are active and sometimes you are not; you have bad emotions, good emotions – this goes on constantly. Then there are qualities and you are aware of space and time. But once prana reaches the Sushumna, it becomes void. In other words: samadhi is attained.

In Hatha Yoga we call this state Unmani avasta. In Raja Yoga it is called Asamprajnata samadhi. In Bhakti Yoga it is called Bhava samadhi. In Jnana Yoga this state is called Nirvikalpa samadhi. But they are all the same thing.

Brahmarandhra means Brahma's Canal. At present, prana goes through Ida and Pingala (through sensual and sexual organs), but when it goes through the Brahmarandhra you will be thinking, "Aham" – "I Am."

Samadhi is also called "burning ground." What are you burning? You are burning all your samskaras (subtle impressions from past lives) which, though hidden, will sprout like seeds in the springtime. When the prana goes into the Sushumna they are burnt.

तस्मात्सर्वप्रयत्नेन प्रबोधयितुमीश्वरीम् ।
ब्रह्मद्वारमुखे सुषां मुद्राभ्यासं समाचरेत् ॥ ५ ॥

(5) *So, the yogi should carefully practice the various mudras to rouse the great goddess (Kundalini) that sleeps, closing the mouth of Sushumna (the doorway to the Absolute).*

महामुद्रा महाबन्धो महावेधश्च खेचरी ।
उड्यानं मूलबन्धश्च बन्धो जालन्धराभिधः ॥ ६ ॥

करणी विपरीताख्या वज्रोली शक्तिचालनम् ।
इदं हि मुद्रादशकं जरामरणनाशनम् ॥ ७ ॥

(6-7) *Maha mudra, Maha bandha, Maha vedha, Khechari, Uddiyana, Mula bandha, Jalandhara bandha, Viparita karani, Vajroli, and Shakti Chalani*

Khechari is the cutting of the tongue. It brings an artificial type of samadhi called Jada samadhi, or inert samadhi; it cannot bring you the highest experience or destroy your desires. It is a way of trying to stop the prana without purification.

Vajroli is the physical contraction which draws water up through the urethra. Then one gradually increases the density of the liquid (by using honey, etc.) so that eventually even a sexual ejaculation can be withdrawn backwards. It is similar to Basti, where water is drawn up into the colon by the vacuum created from performing Nauli. But for our purposes it is not necessary to practice Vajroli because we can get these benefits from Mula bandha by stopping the very impulse.

Uddiyana, Mula and Jalandhara bandhas you already know.

Viparita karani is like the Shoulderstand but in a slanting position. Its purpose is to bring the energy backwards. Generally the nectar is dripping from the moon in the upper area and the sun below is swallowing it all the time. But by inverting the body, this nectar is caught, and then the body remains youthful. That's the theory behind it. Viparita karani should be practiced only in the morning, not in the evening.

To do Shakti chalani, you perform Bhastrika and then you bounce the body up and down.

Before practicing any of these mudras and intense pranayama, you definitely must be very careful about your diet. You also cannot indulge too much in uncontrolled sexual practices as this will bring prana in the wrong direction. So practice celibacy as much as you can, but don't suppress sex; sublimate it. Practice yamas and niyamas, do lots of japa for purification. Then Shakti gets awakened by Shakti chalani like a ripe fruit which is very tasty. But when you take unripe fruit and try to beat it to make it ripe, it may appear to be soft, but it will be sour. The same is true with all spiritual practices. Let it ripen, don't be in a hurry.

these are the ten mudras that destroy old age and death.

Death and old age may be there, but you are not afraid of them since they pertain only to the physical body. There are many siddhas still around who can move about in both the physical and astral worlds. When they come to the physical world, they can take the physical pattern and convert it into a physical body so they can appear before their students. Or if they want to go to other dimensions they can wander around without visa or passport. Saint Narada is an example. He just uses his veena, sings "Om Namo Narayanaya," and he goes to whichever plane he wishes to travel. Sometimes he also comes to the earth plane.

आदिनाथोदितं दिव्यमष्टैश्वर्यप्रदायकम् ।
वल्लभं सर्वसिद्धानां दुर्लभं मरुतामपि ॥ ८ ॥

(8) These were given out by the primeval Lord Siva.
They are divine and confer the eight siddhis.

There are eight [psychic] powers [or siddhis]. But they are not the
purpose of your practice – remember that. They come to test you to
see whether the mind is weak or strong. It is very easy to be tempted.
If you get these siddhis and you demonstrate them once or maybe
twice, then they leave you. Siddhi means energy like electricity, due to
the power built up in the various chakras. If you have a battery, you
can use it for lighting or anything, but when it is used up, it is dead.

So if the siddhis come, you are really in a dangerous situation because
temptation will be very great. All power corrupts, that is the law.
Siddhis are just a distraction for the mind; the prana may be
accumulating, but using siddhis just disperses the prana. Perhaps it
took you several lives to reach a certain level, but just for a few minutes
of pleasure by using siddhis, you fall down to the bottom and have to
start all over again. It is just not worth it. Create siddhis but don't
worry about them; they are not your goal. Anyway, they usually come
only when you don't want them. Sivananda had the eight siddhis, but
he never demonstrated them; he always prostrated before everybody.

They are much sought after by all siddhas, and are
difficult to obtain even by the devas.

Even angels in heaven cannot obtain these powers because they don't
have a physical body. They have an astral body. As they live on the
astral plane, they can't create fresh karma. They live only in heaven
with the karma which they created in their past lives. They have to
wait for thousands of years before they come back to the planet –
again get a human body, again find a good teacher, and again start to
practice. They may not even start, because as they are still living in the

pleasure centers in heaven, when they come back, they may just be born in, say, New York City, where they know only champagne and caviar.

That is why angels are afraid of yogis like you who are practicing and disciplining your life. They are jealous because you go beyond them, so they put obstacles in front of you. They try to tempt you with various types of powers, but they are all obstacles.

गोपनीयं प्रयत्नेन यथा रत्नकरण्डकम् ।
कस्यचिन्नैव वक्तव्यं कुलस्त्रीसुरतं यथा ॥ ९ ॥

(9) This should be carefully kept secret as a box of diamonds. It should not be told to anybody – just as the illicit connection with a married woman of noble family.

The three basic locks and seals are Maha bandha, Maha mudra and Maha vedha. They are very simple to learn, but the Pradipika says to keep them secret – do not give them to everybody. First of all, people will laugh when they hear such things. They won't understand what it means to get the breath into the Sushumna. So do not talk about this to anybody unless they are qualified through practice. Then benefit will come from these three beautiful practices.

At this point I want to talk about the nature of prana and its motion. As the body is not only chemical in its nature, but also electrical, yogis can operate on the electrical body (the energy body) through pranayama, bandhas, and mudras. These operations are all interrelated.

In the beginning of your practice, you tried to purify the nadis through Anuloma Viloma (alternate nostril breathing) with a proportion of 1:4:2. You did this so that the prana (the impulse of life force coming from the brain) might come to a kind of rhythm. (Eventually you can also have rhythm of the apana, but only when you have practiced for a very long time.)

What you discover is not a physical thing, as mudras and bandhas are more subtle than asanas or pranayama. Even a beginner can see the benefits of asanas. Asanas and pranayama operate more on the gross physical level, but they are the road to the mudras and bandhas.

What is called meditation in Raja Yoga, is called "stopping the impulses" in Hatha Yoga. But they are one and the same. If you want to stop the fan, you must turn off the switch so that the electrical impulse will no longer reach the motor which drives the blades. Likewise, what we are trying to do is to turn off the switches to various senses through the power of thought.

Prana accumulates while breathing very gently. At that time, application of the bandhas causes the heartbeat to go down. Also the pulse rate slows down, metabolic activity slows down, and brainwaves go down from beta to alpha. With even greater control of the breath, the brainwaves go down to the theta stage (three to seven cycles per second), and then eventually they stop. So we see that the brain waves change according to the breathing quality.

What we are trying to do with bandhas and mudras is simple to understand. In everyday life we select from among the many sounds we hear as we focus mainly on the sounds which are pleasing to us and try to block unpleasant ones. Examples might be the sound of a jackhammer breaking up a road, or the sound of someone scolding us. We try to block such impulses so that they do not go to the brain and create a negative sensation in the thought atmosphere. We do the same with a horrible sight or with a bad smell such as a skunk odor. We try to shut these off. In the same way, with bandhas and mudras, we are just switching off the impulses going to the brain. We may not be able to shut off everything, but we try to stop as much as possible. In the beginning we have to learn to control by individual "switches," but later on it becomes so habitual that we can just use "remote control." Everything comes to a standstill.

Perhaps you think that some great teacher will touch you and you won't have to practice any asanas, bandhas or mudras. It doesn't usually happen this way; only in rare cases it can happen because of the student's practice of these things in past incarnations. If many of his blocks are gone, the few that remain in the present incarnation can be removed by even a teacher's gaze, a touch, or a word. Then the student reaches the highest samadhi. But as I said before, this is very rare.

पादमूलेन वामेन योनिं सम्पीड्य दक्षिणम्।
प्रसारितं पदं कृत्वा कराभ्यां धारयेद् दृढम्॥ १० ॥

(10) Here Maha mudra is described:
Pressing the perineum with the left heel
and stretching out the right leg,
take hold of the toes (of your
right foot) with your hands.

कण्ठे बन्धं समारोप्य धारयेद्वायुमूर्ध्वतः।
यथा दण्डहतः सर्पो दण्डाकारः प्रजायते॥ ११ ॥

(11) Then contract the throat (in the Jalandhara
bandha) and hold the breath in the upper part (i.e.
in the Sushumna).

ऋज्वीभूता तथा शक्तिः कुण्डली सहसा भवेत्।
तदा सा मरणावस्था जायते द्विपुटाश्रया॥ १२ ॥

(12) Then the Kundalini becomes straight, just as a
coiled snake when struck by a rod suddenly straightens
itself like the stick. Then the two other nadis become
dead, because the breath goes out of them.

ततः शनैः शनैरेव रेचयेन्नैव वेगतः।
इयं खलु महामुद्रा महासिद्धैः प्रदर्शिता॥ १३ ॥

(13) Then one should breathe out very slowly and never quickly. This has been declared to be Maha mudra by the great siddhas.

महाक्लेशादयो दोषा: क्षीयन्ते मरणादय:।
महामुद्रां च तेनैव वदन्ति विबुधोत्तमा:॥ १४॥

(14) This Maha mudra destroys death and such painful factors as the great kleshas. As it had been given out by the great siddhas, it is called Maha mudra or the great mudra, for its excellence.

Brahmananda's Commentary: *The kleshas are five in number, namely avidya (ignorance), asmita (egoism), raga (attachment), dvesha (repulsion) and abhinivesa (clinging to life). The Maha mudra is so called because it seals off (mudra) all pains.*

चन्द्राङ्गे च समभ्यस्य सूर्याङ्गे पुनरभ्यसेत्।
यावत्तुल्या भवेत् सङ्ख्या ततो मुद्रां विसर्जयेत्॥ १५॥

(15) He should practice first on the left side, and then on the right, till both make an equal number. Then (the practice of) the Mudra should be ended (for the time).

Brahmananda's Commentary: *The practice on the left side when the left leg is bent and the right leg stretched and on the right side when the opposite is done.*

न हि पथ्यमपथ्यं वा रसाः सर्वेऽपि नीरसाः।
अपि भुक्तं विषं घोरं पीयूषमिव जीर्यति॥ १६॥

*(16)   (For the practitioner of this) There is nothing
that he cannot eat or must avoid.   All objects of
whatever taste, or having no taste at all, are
digested.   Even poison itself proves to him like nectar.*

क्षयकुष्ठगुदावर्त्तगुल्माजीर्णपुरोगमाः।
तस्य दोषाः क्षयं यान्ति महामुद्रां तु योऽभ्यसेत्॥ १७॥

*(17)   He who practices Maha mudra overcomes
consumption, leprosy, piles, constipation, abdominal
diseases, indigestion, etc.*

कथितेयं महामुद्रा महासिद्धिकरी नृणाम्।
गोपनीया प्रयत्नेन न देया यस्य कस्यचित्॥ १८॥

*(18)   Thus has been described the Maha mudra that
can confer great siddhis upon men.   This should be
carefully kept secret and should not be given out to
any and everybody.*

पार्ष्णिं वामस्य पादस्य योनिस्थाने नियोजयेत्।
वामोरूपरि संस्थाप्य दक्षिणं चरणं तथा॥ १९॥

(19) The Maha bandha is described: Pressing the
perineum with the left heel, place the right foot upon
the left thigh.

पूरयित्वा ततो वायुं हृदये चिबुकं दृढम्।
निष्पीड्य योनिमाकुञ्च्य मनोमध्ये नियोजयेत्॥ २० ॥

(20) Having drawn in the breath,
place the chin firmly on the breast,
contract the anus and fix the mind
on the Sushumna nadi.

धारयित्वा यथाशक्ति रेचयेदनिलं शनैः।
सव्याङ्घ्रे तु समभ्यस्य दक्षाङ्घ्रे पुनरभ्यसेत्॥ २१ ॥

(21) Having restrained the breath as long as
possible, he should then breathe out slowly. He
should practice first on the left side and then on
the right.

मतमत्र तु केषाञ्चित् कण्ठबन्धं विवर्जयेत्।
राजदन्तस्थजिह्वायां बन्धः शस्तो भवेदिति॥ २२ ॥

(22) Some think that the Jalandhara bandha should
be avoided here and that the tongue should be
pressed firmly against the root of the front teeth.

अयं तु सर्वनाडीनामूर्ध्व गतिनिरोधक: ।
अयं खलु महाबन्धो महासिद्धिप्रदायक: ॥ २३ ॥

*(23) This (Jihva bandha in the course of Maha
bandha, that confers great siddhis) stops the upward
course of the prana through all the nadis, except the
Sushumna. This Maha-bandha (helps to) confer
great siddhis.*

कालपाशमहाबन्धविमोचनविचक्षण: ।
त्रिवेणीसङ्गमं धत्ते केदारं प्रापयेन्मन: ॥ २४ ॥

*(24) This frees one from the great noose of King
Yama (Time), and brings about the union of the
three streams (i.e. nadis: Ida, Pingala, and
Sushumna). It also enables the mind to reach Kedara
(the sacred seat of Siva in the mystic centre between
the eyebrows).*

रूपलावण्यसम्पन्ना यथा स्त्री पुरुषं विना ।
महामुद्रामहाबन्धौ निष्फलौ वेधवर्जितौ ॥ २५ ॥

*(25) As a beautiful and graceful woman is unfruitful
without a husband, so Maha mudra and Maha bandha
have no value without the Maha vedha.*

महाबन्धस्थितो योगी कृत्वा पूरकमेकधी:।
वायूनां गतिमावृत्य निभृतं कण्ठमुद्रया॥ २६॥

(26) The Maha vedha is described:
The yogi, assuming the Maha bandha
posture, should draw in his breath with
a concentrated mind, and stop the
upward and downward course of the prana
by the Jalandhara bandha.

समहस्तयुगो भूमौ स्फिचौ सन्ताडयेच्छनै:।
पुट्द्वयमतिक्रम्य वायु: स्फुरति मध्यग:॥ २७॥

(27) Placing his two palms straight upon the ground,
he should strike (the ground) softly with his buttocks.
By this the prana, leaving the two nadis (Ida and
Pingala), goes through the middle (Sushumna).

सोमसूर्याग्निसम्बन्धो जायते चामृताय वै।
मृतावस्था समुत्पन्ना ततो वायुं विरेचयेत्॥ २८॥

(28) Then takes place the union of the moon and
sun and fire (Ida, Pingala and Sushumna) that surely
leads to immortality. The body assumes a deathlike
aspect. Then he should breathe out slowly.

महावेधोऽयमभ्यासान्महासिद्धिप्रदायकः ।
वलीपलितवेपघ्नः सेव्यते साधकोत्तमैः ॥ २९ ॥

(29) This is Maha vedha, and confers great siddhis when practiced. This removes the wrinkles, grey hairs and trembling (consequent on old age). So this is greatly esteemed by the practicer.

एतत्त्रयं महागुह्यं जरामृत्युविनाशनम् ।
वह्निवृद्धिकरं चैव ह्यणिमादिगुणप्रदम् ॥ ३० ॥

(30) These three bandhas that ward off death and old age, increase the gastric fire and confer the siddhis, such as anima, should be carefully kept secret.

अष्टधा क्रियते चैव यामे यामे दिने दिने ।
पुण्यसम्भारसन्धायि पापौघभिदुरं सदा ।
सम्यक् शिक्षावतामेवं स्वल्पं प्रथमसाधनम् ॥ ३१ ॥

(31) These are performed in eight different ways, every day at every yama [three-hour period]. These confer the fullness of virtue and destroy the accumulation of sin (papa). Those who are guided (by the teacher) need practice them gradually.

कपालकुहरे जिह्वा प्रविष्टा विपरीतगा ।
भ्रुवोरन्तर्गता दृष्टिर्मुद्रा भवति खेचरी ॥ ३२ ॥

(32) When the tongue is turned back and enters the cavity leading to the skull, and the eyes are fixed firmly between the eyebrows, this is Khechari.

छेदनचालनदोहै : कलां क्रमेण वर्धयेत्तावत्।
सा यावद् भ्रूमध्यं स्पृशति तदा खेचरीसिद्धि:॥ ३३ ॥

(33) By cutting, shaking and milking the tongue, you should increase its length until it touches the middle of the eyebrows. Then the Khechari mudra succeeds.

[Not recommended. See Commentary on verse 6.]

Brahmananda's Commentary: The cutting is described in the following verses. Shaking it means taking hold of the tongue by the fingers and moving it to and fro. Milking it means taking hold of the tongue and drawing it as one does the udders of a cow in milking it.

स्नुहीपत्रनिभं शस्त्रं सुतीक्ष्णं स्निग्धनिर्मलम्।
समादाय ततस्तेन रोममात्रं समुच्छिनेत्॥ ३४॥

(34) Taking a bright, clean knife as sharp as the leaf of the milkhedge plant, cut to a hair's breadth the fraenum lingum, the tender membrane that connects the tongue with the lower part of the mouth.

[Not recommended. See Commentary on verse 6.]

ततः सैन्धवपथ्याभ्यां चूर्णिताभ्यां प्रधर्षयेत्।
पुनः सप्तदिने प्राप्ते रोममात्रं समुच्छिनेत्॥ ३५॥

*(35) Then rub the part with a compound of
powdered salt and turmeric. Then after seven days,
cut again to the extent of a hair's breadth.*

[Not recommended. See Commentary on verse 6.]

Brahmananda's Commentary: *The compound should be
rubbed on both morning and evening. As salt is prohibited in
the case of Yogis, they substitute the burnt powder of woody
cassia. In the test, salt is mentioned on the assumption that
Khechari mudra should be practised before the beginning of the
Hatha yoga practice. The cutting and medication should be
done twice daily for seven days. On the eighth day, the cut
should be a little deeper. And so on.*

एवं क्रमेण षण्मासं नित्यं युक्तः समाचरेत्।
षण्मासाद्रसनामूलशिराबन्धः प्रणश्यति॥ ३६॥

*(36) He should thus practice daily for a period of six
months. After that the membrane that connects the
tongue with the lower part of the mouth is severed.*

[Not recommended. See Commentary on verse 6.]

कलां पराङ्मुखीं कृत्वा त्रिपथे परियोजयेत्।
सा भवेत् खेचरीमुद्रा व्योमचक्रं तदुच्यते॥ ३७॥

(37) Then turning the tongue, he should make it enter the place at the junction of the three nadis: the hole in the palate. This is called the Khechari mudra. It is also called Vyomachakra.

रसनामूर्ध्वगां कृत्वा क्षणार्धमपि तिष्ठति।
विषैर्विमुच्यते योगी व्याधिमृत्युजरादिभिः॥ ३८॥

(38) The yogi that remains even for half an hour with his tongue turned upwards is freed from poisons, disease, old age and death.

न रोगो मरणं तन्द्रा न निद्रा न क्षुधा तृषा।
न च मूर्च्छा भवेत्तस्य यो मुद्रां वेत्ति खेचरीम्॥ ३९॥

(39) To him who knows the Khechari mudra there is no disease, death, intellectual torpor, sleep, hunger, thirst, or clouding of the intellect.

पीड्यते न स रोगेण लिप्यते न च कर्मणा।
बाध्यते न स कालेन यो मुद्रां वेत्ति खेचरीम्॥ ४०॥

(40) He who knows the Khechari mudra is not affected by any disease. He is not affected by any karma, and Time has no power over him.

Brahmananda's Commentary: *The repetition of the results of Khechari mudra is to impress upon the reader its importance.*

चित्तं चरति खे यस्माज्जिह्वा चरति खे गता।
तेनैषा खेचरी नाम मुद्रा सिद्धैर्निरूपिता॥ ४१॥

(41) This mudra is called Khechari by siddhas because the mind moves in space (Akasha; in the centre of the eyebrows) and the tongue (also) moves the akasha (in the cavity above the palate).

Brahmananda's Commentary: *"Kha" means akasha and "chari" means to move, hence the word Khechari.*

खेचर्या मुद्रितं येन विवरं लम्बिकोर्ध्वतः।
न तस्य क्षरते बिन्दुः कामिन्या-श्लेषितस्य च॥ ४२॥

(42) When one has sealed the cavity at the upper part of the palate through the Khechari mudra, his seminal fluid is not emitted even though he is embraced by a young and passionate woman.

चलितोऽपि यदा बिन्दुः सम्प्राप्तो योनिमण्डलम्।
व्रजत्यूर्ध्वं हतः शक्त्या निबद्धो योनिमुद्रया॥ ४३॥

(43) Even though the fluid has come down to the genital organ, still he can by practicing Yoni mudra, draw it up so that it goes to its place.

Brahmananda's Commentary: *Yoni mudra is another name for Vajroli mudra. As many of these mudras occur in the latter part of the book, I think it necessary to give here a word of caution lest people should take them literally. Though these descriptions of the mudras state as a matter of necessity that these processes are to be undergone through intercourse with females, still I firmly believe that the thing carries on its face its contradiction. We cannot for a moment suppose that the terms "women", "sexual intercourse", and "seminal fluid" are to be understood literally in the case of yogis who have perfected themselves in yama and niyama. Moreover, in the same book, it is stated that only after a certain stage in samadhi is attained, Vajroli mudra, etc., should be practiced. So it seems to me that these refer to some internal mystical processes connected with the development of the mind.*

ऊर्ध्वजिह्व: स्थिरो भूत्वा सोमपानं करोति य:।
मासार्धेन न सन्देहो मृत्युं जयति योगवित्॥ ४४॥

(44) He who with his tongue turned upwards drinks the soma juice with a concentrated mind, he, knowing Yoga, doubtlessly conquers death in 15 days.

[Not recommended. See commentary on verse 6.]

Brahmananda's Commentary: *Above the palate, the Moon is said to be situated, and the nectar that flows from her falls down and is consumed by the Sun that is near the navel. But if he now stops the flow of nectar by closing the hole in the palate of his mouth, it prevents the decay of the body. "Soma" means Moon.*

नित्यं सोमकलापूर्णं शरीरं यस्य योगिन:।
तक्षकेणापि दष्टस्य विषं तस्य न सर्पति॥ ४५॥

(45) In the case of the yogi who fills his body daily with the nectar flowing from the moon, even though he is bitten by the serpent Takshaka, the poison does not spread throughout his body.

Brahmananda's Commentary: *Takshaka, possessing most virulent poison, is one of the eight serpent kings in the Patala, the greatest of whom is Sesha or Ananta.*

इन्धनानि यथा वह्निस्तैलवर्तिं च दीपकः।
तथा सोमकलापूर्णं देही देहं न मुञ्चति ॥ ४६ ॥

(46) As the fire does not go out so long as there is fuel, as the light in the lamp does not die out so long as there is oil and wick, so also the Jiva [individual soul] remains in the body as long as it is vivified by the nectar of the Moon.

गोमांसं भक्षयेन्नित्यं पिबेदमरवारुणीम्।
कुलीनं तमहं मन्ये चेतरे कुलघातकाः ॥ ४७ ॥

(47) He may eat daily gomamsa (literally the flesh of a cow) and he may drink amaravaruni (literally strong liquor), but I consider him to be born in the most noble of families.

[Not to be taken literally. See next verse.]

Brahmananda's Commentary: *The words in the test, gomamsa and Amaravaruni, are explained in the next two verses.*

गोशब्देनोदिता जिह्वा तत्प्रवेशो हि तालुनि।
गोमांसभक्षणं   तत्तु   महापातकनाशनम् ॥ ४८ ॥

*(48) By the word "go" is meant the tongue.
Making it enter the hole in the palate is "eating the
flesh of the go" (cow or the tongue). This destroys
the five great sins.*

Brahmananda's Commentary: *The five great sins are said to
be: killing a brahmana, drinking intoxicating liquor, theft,
adultary with the wife of a teacher, and associating with anyone
guilty of these sins.*

जिह्वाप्रवेशसम्भूतवह्निनोत्पादित: खलु।
चन्द्रात् स्रवति य: सार: स स्यादमरवारुणी ॥ ४९ ॥

*(49) The nectar which flows from the moon because
of the heat produced by the entry of the tongue, that
is called Amaravaruni.*

Brahmananda's Commentary: *The term "varuni" means
wine. In the above two stanzas is given an excellent instance of
the way in which the Hindu occult writers veil their real
meaning under apparently absurd symbols. The principle
seems to be this. They thought that the very absurdity of the
symbol and its inconsistence with the subject in hand, would
force the reader to think that there was something under it, and
so he should look deeper for an explanation of this absurdity. A
misconception of this rule seems to have given rise to many
absurd interpretations of really occult symbols, and many*

*negative practices that encourage animal tendencies and
passions. Examples of this may be multiplied, such as the
relations between Krishna and Radha and the sixteen thousand
gopis or cowherdesses; the five Pandava brothers marrying one
woman (Draupadi); the stories of rishis marrying wives and
begetting children of mature understanding within an
inconceivably short time; and the whole mystic terminology of
the tantras that has given rise to so many disgusting practices.*

चुम्बन्ती यदि लम्बिकाग्रमनिशं जिह्वारसस्पन्दिनी,
    सक्षारा कटुकाम्लदुग्धसदृशी मध्वाज्यतुल्या तथा।
व्याधीनां हरणं जरान्तकरणं शस्त्रागमोदीरणं,
    तस्य स्यादमरत्वमष्टगुणितं सिद्धाङ्गनाकर्षणम्॥ ५० ॥

*(50) If the tongue which is capable of producing
the nectar rays (of the Moon) that taste salty,
pungent and sharp, and also resemble milk, honey
and ghee in taste, remains pressed into the hole in
the palate, all the diseases are destroyed, and (also)
old age. This act enables him to give out all the
Vedas and sciences, to ward off weapons of every
sort, confers on him immortality and the eight
siddhis, and gives him power to attract the damsels
of the siddhas.*

[Not to be taken literally.]

The nectar possesses the tastes of salt, chilli, tamarind, milk, honey,
and ghee, as if it were these things. The tastes vary according to the
times.

मूर्ध्न: षोडशपत्रपद्मगलितं प्राणादवासं हठा-
    दूर्ध्वास्यो रसनां नियम्य विवरे शक्तिं परां चिन्तयन्।
उत्कल्लोलकलाजलं च विमलं धारामयं य: पिबे-
    त्रिव्याधि: स मृणालकोमलवपुर्योगी चिरं जीवति॥ ५१॥

*(51) He who, with upturned face and tongue closing
the hole in the palate, contemplates upon the
Supreme Power (Kundalini, Parashakti), and drinks
the clear waves of the stream of nectar flowing from
the Moon in the head, into the sixteen-petaled lotus
(in the throat), through the control over prana during
Hatha Yoga practice, becomes a yogi freed from all
diseases, and lives long with a body soft and
beautiful as the fibers of a lotus stem.*

यत्प्रालेयं प्रहितसुषिरं मेरुमूर्धान्तरस्थं
    तस्मिंस्तत्त्वं प्रवदति सुधीस्तन्मुखं निम्नगानाम्।
चन्द्रात्सार: स्रवति वपुषस्तेन मृत्युर्नराणां
    तद्बध्नीयात् सुकरणमतो नान्यथा कार्यसिद्धि:॥ ५२॥

*(52) In the interior of the upper part of Meru (i.e.
Sushumna) in the cavity, which is the fountainhead
of the nadis, nectar is secreted. The person, with his
intellect of the pure sattva cast, unclouded by rajas
and tamas, sees therein the Truth (his own Atman).
It (the hole) is the mouth through which the rivers
(nadis) discharge themselves. From the Moon there*

*flows nectar, the essence of the body, and hence the
death of the mortals. So one should practice the
beneficial Khechari mudra. If not, there can be no
Kaya siddhi (endowing the body with beauty, grace,
strength and adamantine firmness).*

सुषिरं ज्ञानजनकं पञ्चस्रोत:समन्वितम्।
तिष्ठते खेचरी मुद्रा तस्मिञ्शून्ये निरञ्जने ॥ ५३ ॥

*(53) The Sushumna, especially the hole therein, is
the meeting place of the five rivers, and confers
divine knowledge. In the void of that hole, that is
free from the effects of avidya (ignorance), grief and
delusion, the Khechari mudra becomes perfect.*

Brahmananda's Commentary: *The rivers referred to in the
above stanzas mean so many nadis: Ida, Pingala, Sushumna,
Gandhara, which stand for the rivers Ganges, Jamuna,
Saraswati, Narmada, etc.*

एकं सृष्टिमयं बीजमेका मुद्रा च खेचरी।
एको देवो निरालम्ब एकावस्था मनोन्मनी ॥ ५४ ॥

*(54) There is only one germ of evolution (i.e. OM).
There is only one mudra: Khechari; only one deity,
i.e., the one that does not depend on anything; and
only one avastha or spiritual state, i.e., Manomani.*

Brahmananda's Commentary: *As the other things said are the most important of their class, so Khechari is the best of mudras.*

बद्धो येन सुषुम्नायां प्राणस्तूड्डीयते यतः।
तस्मादुड्डीयनाख्योऽयं योगिभिः समुदाहतः॥ ५५॥

(55) Uddiyana bandha is so called by the yogis, because when practiced, the prana flies through the Sushumna.

उड्डीनं कुरुते यस्मादविश्रान्तं महाखगः।
उड्डीयानं तदेव स्यात्तत्र बन्धोऽमिधीयते॥ ५६॥

(56) Because through this bandha, the great bird Prana flies incessantly through the Sushumna, it is called Uddiyana bandha. This bandha is now explained.

Brahmananda's Commentary: *Uddiyana comes from the Sanskrit "ut" and "di," meaning "to fly up."*

उदरे पश्चिमं तानं नाभेरूर्ध्वं च कारयेत्।
उड्डीयानो ह्यसौ बन्धो मृत्युमातङ्गकेसरी॥ ५७॥

(57) The drawing up of the intestines above and below the navel (so that they rest against the back of the body high up the thorax) is called Uddiyana bandha, and is the lion that kills the elephant "Death."

Brahmananda's Commentary: *In this bandha, the stomach appears very slender and could be compressed within a handspan. The process seems to be this: by a very strong expiration, the lungs are emptied and driven against the upper part of the thorax, carrying the diaphragm along with them. Then the intestines are taken up and fill the vacant space.*

उड्डीयानं तु सहजं गुरुणा कथितं सदा।
अभ्यसेत्सततं यस्तु वृद्धोऽपि तरुणायते ॥ ५८ ॥

(58) He who constantly practices Uddiyana bandha as taught by his guru, so that it becomes natural, even though he is old, becomes young.

"Becomes natural" means that it follows naturally after powerful expiration.

नाभेरूर्ध्वमधश्चापि तानं कुर्यात्प्रयत्नतः।
षण्मासमभ्यसेन्मृत्युं जयत्येव न संशयः ॥ ५९ ॥

(59) He should draw back with effort (the abdomen) above and below the navel, and practise for six months. (Then) without doubt, he conquers death in six months.

सर्वेषामेव   बन्धानामुत्तमो   ह्युड्डियानकः।
उड्डियाने दृढे बन्धे मुक्तिः स्वाभाविकी भवेत् ॥ ६० ॥

(60) *Of all the bandhas, the Uddiyana is the most excellent. When this has been mastered, mukti or emancipation follows naturally.*

Brahmananda's Commentary: *When the Uddiyana bandha has been mastered, the Prana flows up through the Sushumna and reaches the Brahmarandhra. This results in Samadhi and leads to liberation.*

पार्ष्णिभागेन सम्पीड्य योनिमाकुञ्चयेद्गुदम् ।
अपानमूर्ध्वमाकृष्य   मूलबन्धोऽभिधीयते ॥ ६१ ॥

(61) *Pressing the perineum with the heel, contract the anus and draw the apana upwards. This is Mula bandha.*

अधोगतिमपानं वा   ऊर्ध्वगं कुरुते बलात् ।
आकुञ्चनेन तं प्राहुर्मूलबन्धं हि योगिनः ॥ ६२ ॥

(62) *Because by contraction of the Muladhara, the apana whose course is downwards, is made to go upwards (through Sushumna). Therefore the yogis call it Mula bandha.*

गुदं पाष्ण्या तु सम्पीड्य वायुमाकुञ्चयेद्बलात् ।
वारं वारं   यथा चोर्ध्वं समायाति समीरणः ॥ ६३ ॥

(63) *Pressing the anus with the heel, contract the air forcibly and repeatedly, until the breath (Apana) goes upwards.*

प्राणापानौ नादबिन्दू मूलबन्धेन चैकताम्।
गत्वा योगस्य संसिद्धिं यच्छतो नात्र संशय:॥ ६४ ॥

*(64) Through the Mula bandha, prana and apana,
nada and bindu unite and obtain perfection in Yoga.
There is no doubt about this.*

Brahmananda's Commentary: *The meaning seems to be
this: Through the Mula bandha, the prana and apana unite
and go into the Sushumna. Then the inner sounds become
distinct and the prana and apana uniting with nada go over the
heart and join the bindu, i.e. the anusvara or the inaudible
sound of the point in the sacred syllable OM, symbolizing the
transcendent Siva. They then proceed to the head and thus the
yogi obtains perfection. Nada is the mystical inner sound
proceeding from the Anahata chakra or the Cardiac plexus.*

अपानप्राणयोरैक्यं क्षयो मूत्रपुरीषयो:।
युवा भवति वृद्धोऽपि सततं मूलबन्धनात्॥ ६५ ॥

*(65) By constant practice of Mula bandha, a union
of the prana and the apana is achieved. Urine and
excrement decrease considerably and even the aged
become young.*

When you properly perform pranayama with bandhas and mudras,
along with the right diet, your urination and other excretions become
very limited. There is just a little perspiration. This is because there is
not much gross poison left in the system.

अपाने ऊर्ध्वगे जाते प्रयाते वह्निमण्डलम्।
तदाऽनलशिखा दीर्घा जायते वायुनाऽऽहता ॥ ६६ ॥

*(66) When the apana rises upwards and reaches the
circle of fire, then the flame of the fire grows long
and bright, being fanned by apana.*

This is to be taken symbolically so that you can get a mental picture of
how the Kundalini functions. The fire is the Kundalini. Just as the fire
becomes bigger when it is fanned by the wind, so when the prana and
apana are united, this starts to fan the Kundalini. It becomes brighter.

> **Brahmananda's Commentary:** *[In human beings] the seat of
> fire is triangular in shape and is situated in the center of the
> body, below the navel. In the case of animals it is rectangular,
> and circular in the case of birds. The flame of the fire referred
> to is the gastric fire.*

ततो यातो वह्न्यपानौ प्राणमुष्णस्वरूपकम्।
तेनात्यन्तप्रदीप्तस्तु ज्वलनो देहजस्तथा ॥ ६७ ॥

*(67) When the apana and the fire join prana, which
is naturally hot, then the heat in the body becomes
considerably bright and powerful.*

This is not physical heat; it is psychic heat, and you can see the
radiations. It is said that a true yogi's body will shine even in advanced
age. There will be no wrinkles.

तेन कुण्डलिनी सुप्ता सन्तप्ता सम्प्रबुध्यते।
दण्डाहता भुजङ्गीव निश्वस्य ऋजुतां ब्रजेत् ॥ ६८ ॥

*(68) By reason of that, the Kundalini which is
asleep, feeling the extreme heat, awakens just as a
serpent struck by a stick hisses and straightens itself.*

Again, this symbolizes awakening of the Kundalini. Of course there is
no serpent there. The energy which is dormant (static), becomes
kinetic (or dynamic).

बिलं प्रविष्टेव ततो ब्रह्मनाड्यन्तरं व्रजेत् ।
तस्मान्नित्यं मूलबन्ध: कर्त्तव्यो योगिभि: सदा ॥ ६९ ॥

*(69) Then it goes into its hole, i.e. the interior of
Sushumna. Therefore, the yogis should always
practice Mula bandha.*

"Always" means that you concentrate. Breathing from the bottom, feel
that the Kundalini is going up, all the while repeating your mantra.

कण्ठमाकुञ्च्य हृदये स्थापयेच्चिबुकं दृढम् ।
बन्धो जालन्धराख्योऽयं जरामृत्युविनाशक: ॥ ७० ॥

*(70) Contract the throat and press the chin firmly
against the breast (four inches from the heart). This
is Jalandhara bandha, and destroys old age
and death.*

बध्नाति हि शिराजालमधोगामि नभोजलम् ।
ततो जालन्धरो बन्ध: कण्ठदु:खौघनाशन: ॥ ७१ ॥

(71) It is called Jalandhara bandha because it tightens the network (jala) of nadis and stops the downward course of the ambrosial water (jala) flowing from the hole in the palate. This bandha destroys the pains arising in the throat.

जालन्धरे कृते बन्धे कण्ठसङ्कोचलक्षणे ।
न पीयूषं पतत्यग्नौ न च वायु: प्रकुप्यति ॥ ७२ ॥

(72) When the Jalandhara bandha is assumed and the throat contracted, no drop of the nectar falls into the gastric fire, and the prana does not go in the wrong way, i.e., in the space between the nadis.

कण्ठसङ्कोचनेनैव द्वे नाड्यौ स्तम्भयेद् दृढम् ।
मध्यचक्रमिदं ज्ञेयं षोडशाधारबन्धनम् ॥ ७३ ॥

(73) By the firm contraction of the throat, the two nadis are deadened. Here in the throat is situated the middle chakra, the Vishuddha. This binds firmly the sixteen adharas or vital centers.

Brahmananda's Commentary: *They are the toes, ankles, knees, thighs, the perinium, the generative organs, the navel, the heart, the neck, the throat, the palate, the nose, the center of the eyebrows, the forehead, the skull, and the Brahmarandhra, i.e., the upper opening of the Sushumna nadi in the skull.*

मूलस्थानं समाकुञ्च्य उड्डियानं तु कारयेत् ।
इडां च पिङ्गलां बध्वा वाहयेत् पश्चिमे पथि ॥ ७४ ॥

*(74) Contracting the anus, practice the Uddiyana
bandha. Tighten firmly the Ida and the Pingala (by
Jalandhara bandha), and cause the breath to flow
through the upper path, i.e. Sushumna.*

अनेनैव विधानेन प्रयाति पवनालयम् ।
ततो न जायते मृत्युर्जरारोगादिकं तथा ॥ ७५ ॥

*(75) By these means the breath becomes absorbed
(remains motionless in the Sushumna). Then there is
no disease, old age or death.*

बन्धत्रयमिदं श्रेष्ठं महासिद्धैश्च सेवितम् ।
सर्वेषां हठतन्त्राणां साधनं योगिनो विदुः ॥ ७६ ॥

*(76) Yogis know these three excellent bandhas
practiced by the great siddhas (Matsyendra, Vasishta
and others), and which confer the siddhis laid down
in the treatises of Hatha Yoga.*

यत्किञ्चित्स्रवते चन्द्रादमृतं दिव्यरूपिणः ।
तत्सर्वं ग्रसते सूर्यस्तेन पिण्डो जरायुतः ॥ ७७ ॥

(77) Here Viparita Karani is described: Every particle of nectar (the Saytravi) that flows from the ambrosial Moon is swallowed up by the Sun. Hence the body becomes old.

Brahmananda's Commentary: *Just as the Moon is situated at the root of the palate and pours down a stream of nectar, so the all-consuming Sun is situated near the navel and swallows the ambrosial flow.*

According to the Yoga system, we get old because the ambrosial energy coming from the higher centers is swallowed by the Sun. It is just like water dripping into a fire. Every day, from consuming this energy, eventually old age results. But if you reverse this process by stopping the flow for a certain time, then the Sun won't swallow the energy. There is no way that I can explain this properly in scientific terms because we are not talking about physical energy, but about astral or psychic waves. The "all-consuming Sun" is the fire center at the navel. We stop this flow with the practice of Viparita karani as described below.

तत्रास्ति करणं दिव्यं सूर्यस्य मुखवञ्चनम् ।
गुरूपदेशतो ज्ञेयं न तु शास्त्रार्थकोटिभि: ॥ ७८ ॥

(78) There is a most excellent process by which the Sun is deceived. This should be learned from the guru himself. A theoretical study of crores of shastras [scriptures] cannot throw any light upon it.

Here they are giving you a warning. It is not a mere physical process which is being described below, but it is the movement of psychic energy (prana and apana). Moreover, it is not the physical Sun and the physical Moon which was referred to above; they are psychic phenomena. Words cannot explain these things so you must learn from a guru.

ऊर्ध्वं नाभेरधस्तालोरूर्ध्वं भानुरध: शशी।
करणी विपरीताख्या गुरुवाक्येन लभ्यते ॥ ७९ ॥

*(79) This is known as Viparita
karani. It consists in making the
Sun and the Moon assume exactly
their reverse positions, i.e. the Sun
that is now below the navel, and the
Moon that is above the palate,
change places. This is to be learned from the guru.*

नित्यमभ्यासयुक्तस्य　　　जठराग्निविवर्धिनी।
आहरो बहुलस्तस्य सम्पाद्य: साधकस्य च ॥ ८० ॥

*(80) In the case of a man who practices this daily,
the gastric fire is increased. Therefore, the practicer
should always have a large quantity of food ready.*

That you all don't mind at all, I know. Actually, this should be
understood to mean nutritious food.

अल्पाहारो यदि　भवेदग्निर्दहति　तत्क्षणात्।
अध: शिराश्चोर्ध्वपाद: क्षणं स्यात् प्रथमे दिने ॥ ८१ ॥

*(81) If he stints on his diet, the fire consumes
the body.*

This means that you should not fast while following intensive practice

On the first day, he should stand for a moment upon his head, with his heels in the air. This is called Viparita karani.

Brahmananda's Commentary: *The process seems to be this. The body should be raised in the air by resting the crown of the head and shoulders upon the ground, and supporting the hips with the hands, the elbows resting on the ground (if required).*

This differs from the shoulderstand, since in the shoulderstand the pressure is on the Vishuddha chakra as well as on the thyroid and parathyroid glands. Here, as there is no pressure on those places, the pranic energy flows.

क्षणाच्च किञ्चिदधिकमभ्यसेच्च दिने दिने।
वलितं पलितं चैव षण्मासोर्ध्वं न दृश्यते।
याममात्रं तु यो नित्यमभ्यसेत् स तु कालजित्॥ ८२॥

(82) While practicing this, increase the duration gradually every day. After six months, wrinkles and gray hair disappear. He who practices this for a yama (three hours daily) conquers death.

स्वेच्छया वर्तमानोऽपि योगोक्तैर्नियमैर्विना।
वज्रोलीं यो विजानाति स योगी सिद्धिभाजनम्॥ ८३॥

(83) If anyone, though living an ordinary life without observing yama and niyama as laid down by Yoga, practices the Vajroli mudra, he becomes the repository of the siddhis.

(84-103) [These verses have been omitted, as they describe Vajroli, Sahajoli, and Amaroli mudras, practices which are not followed in sattvic sadhana.]

कुटिलाङ्गी कुण्डलिनी भुजङ्गी शक्तिरीश्वरी।
कुण्डल्यरुन्धती चैते शब्दाः पर्यायवाचकाः॥ १०४॥

(104) Now I describe the Shakti chalani kriya. The Kutilangi, the Kundalini, the Bhujangi, the Shakti, the Ishwari, the Kundalini, and the Arundhati are all names for the same Shakti.

उद्घाटयेत्कपाटं तु यथा कुञ्चिकया हठात्।
कुण्डलिन्या तथा योगी मोक्षद्वारं विभेदयेत्॥ १०५॥

(105) As one forces open a door with a key, so the yogi should force open the door of moksha [i.e. the Sushumna] by the [power of] Kundalini.

येन मार्गेण गन्तव्यं ब्रह्मस्थानं निरामयम्।
मुखेनाच्छाद्य तद्द्वारं प्रसुप्ता परमेश्वरी॥ १०६॥

(106) The Parameshwari (Great Goddess) sleeps, closing with her mouth the hole through which one should go to the Brahmarandhra (the seat of Brahman), where there is no pain or misery.

कन्दोर्ध्वे कुण्डलीशक्ति: सुप्ता मोक्षाय योगिनाम्।
बन्धनाय च मूढानां यस्तां वेत्ति स योगवित्॥ १०७॥

(107) *The Kundalini sleeps above the kanda
(the place near the navel where the nadis unite
and separate). It gives mukti to the yogis and
bondage to the fools.*

Brahmananda's Commentary: *The kanda is the place between
the naval and the scrotum from where spring 72,000 Nadis. See
verse 113 below.*

When the Kundalini is dormant, in a low vibratory state, you only
understand sensual and sexual life. But when it is in a subtle state it
gives liberation.

He who knows her, knows Yoga.

He knows the Shakti which is hidden in all of us.

कुण्डली कुटिलाकारा सर्पवत्परिकीर्त्तिता।
सा शक्तिश्चालिता येन स मुक्तो नात्र संशय:॥ १०८॥

(108) *The Kundalini is described as being coiled like
a serpent. He who causes that Shakti to move (from
the Muladhara upwards) becomes free, without doubt.*

गङ्गायमुनयोर्मध्ये बालरण्डां तपस्विनीम्।
बलात्कारेण गृह्णीयात्तद्विष्णो: परमं पदम्॥ १०९॥

(109) Between the Ganges and the Jamuna, there sits the young widow, practising austerity. She should be seized by force. That leads to the Supreme seat of Vishnu.

If you are a yogi, you must be able to correctly interpret such things. See next verse.

इडा भगवती गङ्गा पिङ्गला यमुना नदी ।
इडापिङ्गलयोर्मध्ये बालरण्डा च कुण्डली ॥ ११० ॥

(110) Ida is the sacred Ganges, and Pingala is the Jamuna. Between Ida and Pingala there sits the young widow, Kundalini.

Why is the Kundalini Shakti called "widow" here? It is because she is not with Siva. Siva is in the Sahasrara, so she is alone, a widow. Simple language is used, but it is all very difficult for Westerners to understand on their own.

पुच्छे प्रगृह्य भुजगीं सुषामुद्बोधयेच्च ताम् ।
निद्रां विहाय सा शक्तिरूर्ध्वमुत्तिष्ठते हठात् ॥ १११ ॥

(111) You should awake the sleeping serpent (Kundalini) by taking hold of its tail. That Shakti, leaving off sleep, goes up forcibly.

How do you take hold and shake its tail? By bandhas and mudras.

Brahmananda's Commentary: *The secret of this process must be learnt from a guru.*

अवस्थिता चैव फणावती सा प्रातश्च सायं प्रहरार्धमात्रम्।
प्रपूर्य सूर्यात् परिधानयुक्त्या प्रगृह्य नित्यं परिचालनीया॥ ११२॥

*(112) Having inspired [inhaled] through the right
nostril (Pingala), the recumbent serpent should be taken
hold of by the process of paridhara, and made to move
daily for an hour and a half, both morning and evening.*

This refers to Alternate Nostril Breathing, Surya bheda, and other pranayamas.

Then he should manipulate this Shakti for about an hour and a half at both morning and evening twilights.

You must shake the "tail" for an hour and a half.

Brahmananda's Commentary: *This process of paridhara
should be learnt from a guru. The process is the movement of
the abdominal muscle from left to right and right to left in a
spiral.*

Note: see The Serpent Power, 1964, p. 207.

ऊर्ध्वं वितस्तिमात्रं तु विस्तारं चतुरङ्गुलम्।
मृदुलं धवलं प्राक्तं वेष्टिताम्बरलक्षणम्॥ ११३॥

*(113) The kanda is twelve inches above the anus
and four inches both ways in extension.*

It is the approximate area where all the plexuses are joined together at the Muladhara. This is where the energy is dormant.

*It has been described to be of a round shape, and
covered as if with a soft and white piece of cloth.*

It is soft and white because in the spinal cord there is also white matter.
This was written thousands of years ago.

Brahmananda's Commentary: *Two inches above the anus
and two below the penis in the middle of the body, the kanda is
nine inches from the middle of the body. It is like an egg and is
covered by membranous coverings. In the case of beasts and
birds it is the middle of the abdomen.*

This is because their spinal cords are quite different. [From the kanda
spring the 72,000 nadis.] This is like a battery, with wires going to
numerous areas. This is why, when the nadis are not purified properly
by bandhas and pranayama, etc., the prana goes through wrong nadis
and you get psychological problems.

सति वज्रासने पादौ कराभ्यां धारयेद् दृढम्।
गुल्फदेशसमीपे च कन्दं तत्र प्रपीडयेत्॥ ११४॥

*(114) Seated on the Vajrasana posture, firmly take
hold of the feet near the ankles and thereby put
pressure on the kanda.*

This is really what we call Siddhasana; sometimes it was called
Vajrasana by different teachers. This is because "Vajrasana" literally
means "energy asana," so it was applied to any asana which was used for
the raising of the energy. Vajra was the thunderbolt weapon of Indra.

वज्रासने स्थितो योगी चालयित्वा च कुण्डलीम्।
कुर्यादन्नतरं भस्त्रां कुण्डलीमाशु बोधयेत्॥ ११५॥

(115) Assuming the Vajrasana [Siddhasana] posture, the yogi having caused the Kundalini to move. He should then perform the Bhastrika kumbhaka. Thus he will soon awaken the Kundalini.

This is Shakti chalani.

भानोराकुञ्चनं कुर्यात् कुण्डलीं चालयेत् तत: ।
मृत्युवक्त्रगतस्यापि तस्य मृत्युभयं कुत: ॥ ११६ ॥

(116) He should then contract the Sun (that is near the navel), and then cause the Kundalini to move.

What is meant by "contract the sun?" Uddiyana bandha. This is an extremely advanced practice, after years of training. It is not necessary to go too deeply into this subject here. If this is practiced early there will be no results because of the existence of blocks and impurities in the Sushumna.

Even though he is in the mouth of death, he need not fear it. When the energy is in the Sushumna, there is no death for him.

Brahmananda's Commentary: *Contracting the abdomen, he contracts the Sun.*

मुहूर्त्तद्वयपर्यन्तं   निर्भयं   चालनादसौ ।
ऊर्ध्वमाकृष्यते किञ्चित् सुषुम्नायां समुद्गता ॥ ११७ ॥

(117) By moving the Kundalini fearlessly for about an hour and a half, she is drawn upwards a little through the Sushumna.

Waves of energy start moving, slowly, slowly upwards.

तेन कुण्डलिनी तस्या: सुषुम्नाया मुखं ध्रुवम्।
जहाति तस्मात् प्राणोऽयं सुषुम्नां व्रजति स्वत:॥ ११८॥

(118) By this process, Kundalini certainly leaves open the mouth of the Sushumna, and the prana goes naturally through it.

तस्मात् सञ्चालयेन्नित्यं सुखसुप्तामरुन्धतीम्।
तस्या: संचालनेनैव योगी रोगै: प्रमुच्यते॥ ११९॥

(119) So one should move daily the Arundhati (Kundalini) that is calmly sleeping. By moving her, the yogi is freed from diseases.

येन सञ्चालिता शक्ति: स योगी सिद्धिभाजनम्।
किमत्र बहुनोक्तेन कालं   जयति लीलया॥ १२०॥

(120) The yogi that moves the Shakti becomes the possessor of the siddhis. What is the use of speaking about it? He conquers time (death) playfully.

Mere speaking is not sufficient, you must practice.

ब्रह्मचर्यरतस्यैव   नित्यं   हितमिताशिन: ।
मण्डलाद् दृश्यते सिद्धि: कुण्डल्यभ्यासयोगिन:॥ १२१ ॥

*(121) Only a yogi leading the life of a brahmachari
(celibate)and observing a moderate and nutritious
diet obtains perfection in the manipulation of
Kundalini within forty days.*

This is possible only if many of your impurities have been removed in
past incarnations. Then, a bit of practice and perhaps an "OM" from
the guru, might be sufficient for this to take place. But if it doesn't
happen, you just keep practicing your sadhana until you find success
in your next life or in your tenth life from now. Sometimes your old
karma may come and create all kinds of obstacles such as sicknesses,
etc. Sometimes the karma burns very slowly. When you start intense
sadhana, then things may become very intense for you. You may think
that you are getting worse, but actually you are burning your karma
very quickly in a very short time. Whenever I go into seclusion, most
of my karma comes up to be burnt out. I developed frostbite, an
accident to my knee, and other things.

कुण्डलीं चालयित्वा तु भस्त्रां कुर्याद्विशेषत:।
एवमभ्यस्यतो नित्यं यमिनो यमभी: कुत:॥ १२२ ॥

*(122) Having set the Kundalini in motion, he should
practice the Bhastrika kumbhaka constantly. The
person perfected in yama, and practicing this, need
never fear death.*

द्वासप्ततिसहस्राणां नाडीनां मलशोधने।
कुत: प्रक्षालनोपाय: कुण्डल्यभ्यसनादृते॥ १२३ ॥

*(123) Except the practice of (causing to move)
Kundalini (through Shakti chalini), what other means
is there for clearing away the impurities of the
72,000 nadis?*

इयं तु मध्यमा नाडी दृढाभ्यासेन योगिनाम्।
आसनप्राणसंयाममुद्राभि: सरला भवेत्॥ १२४ ॥

*(124) This middle nadi (Sushumna) becomes
straight (for the easy passage of prana) by
persevering practice, and by the asanas, pranayamas
and mudras.*

अभ्यासे तु विनि द्राणां मनोधृत्वा समाधिना।
रुद्राणी वा परा मुद्रा भद्रां सिद्धिं प्रयच्छति॥ १२५ ॥

*(125) He who, with his mind firmly concentrated,
practices this without sloth, obtains through the
Shambhavi or any other mudra, various siddhis.*

राजयोगं विना पृथ्वी राजयोगं विना निशा।
राजयोगं विना मुद्रा विचित्रापि न शोभते॥ १२६ ॥

(126) There is no Prithvi (earth) without the Raja Yoga. There is no night without the Raja Yoga. The various mudras become useless without the Raja Yoga.

Brahmananda's Commentary: *Here Prithvi stands for firmness of the asanas. Night stands for kumbhaka, in which state everything is quiet. There is a pun on the words 'Raja Yoga.' The earth does not flourish without the sovereign's rule (Raja Yoga), the night does not shine in the absence of the moon (raja) and the seal (mudra) is of no use without being associated with the king (raja).*

मारुतस्य विधिं सर्वं मनोयुक्तं समभ्यसेत् ।
इतरत्र न कर्त्तव्या मनोवृत्तिर्मनीषिणा ॥ १२७ ॥

(127) All the processes with regard to the breath should be gone through with a mind concentrated on the subject. The wise man should not allow his mind to wander away during that time.

इति मुद्रा दश प्रोक्ता आदिनाथेन शम्भुना ।
एकैका तासु यमिनां महासिद्धिप्रदायिनी ॥ १२८ ॥

(128) Thus have the ten mudras been described by the Adinatha (Lord Siva). By any one of these, one possessed of self-restraint might obtain great siddhis.

उपदेशं हि मुद्राणां यो दत्ते साम्प्रदायिकम् ।
स एव श्री गुरु: स्वामी साक्षादीश्वर एव स: ॥ १२९ ॥

(129)   He who teaches the secret of these mudras
as handed down from guru to guru is the real guru,
and can be called Ishwara in human form.

तस्य वाक्यपरो भूत्वा मुद्राभ्यासे समाहितः।
अणिमादि गुणैः सार्धं लभते कालवञ्चनम्॥ १३० ॥

(130)   The person following carefully the words of the
guru, and attentively practicing the mudras, obtains the
siddhis: anima, etc., as also the art of deceiving death.

हठयोगप्रदीपिका

hatha yoga pradipika

CHAPTER FOUR

नम: शिवाय गुरवे नादबिन्दुकलात्मने।
निरञ्जनपदं याति नित्यं यत्र परायण:॥ १ ॥

*(1) Salutations to Siva the guru, who is of the form
of nada, bindu and kala; the person ever-devoted to
these obtains the stainless state [free from Maya].*

CHAPTER FOUR

नम: शिवाय गुरवे नादबिन्दुकलात्मने।
निरञ्जनपदं याति नित्यं यत्र परायण:॥ १ ॥

(1) Salutations to Siva the guru, who is of the form of nada, bindu and kala;

Nada means sound or wave energy. Bindu means dot; here the dot is the center or the nucleus. Kala means that which is the transcendental wave; it ends with a timeless state, a spaceless state, a non-dual state. Nada and bindu are like Siva and Shakti. Bindu is like the nucleus in an atom, nada is the electrons whirling around the nucleus, and the energy is kala. When the nada and bindu are changed into its wavelength, it becomes energy: a pure wave. Lord Siva has condensed everything: nada (the sound energy), bindu (the static force), and kala (the transcendental energy).

the person ever-devoted to these obtains the stainless state [free from Maya].

Brahmananda's Commentary: *This chapter is wholly devoted to Raja Yoga. The nada is a mystical sound similar to the prolongation of the sound of a bell, and is represented by the semicircle in OM. Bindu is the "m" sound of the anusvara in the Pranava. Kala is a specialty of nada.*

अथेदानीं प्रवक्ष्यामि समाधिक्रममुत्तमम्।
मृत्युघ्नं च सुखोपायं ब्रह्मानन्दकरं परम्॥ २ ॥

*(2)   Now I shall expound the excellent process of
samadhi that destroys death, leads to eternal bliss and
brings on the Supreme Bliss of (absorption in) Brahman.*

In [Raja] Yoga there are eight steps. We have been considering asanas,
pranayama, dharana, dhyana, etc., and now we come to samadhi, the
final stage. According to Hatha Yoga, these eight steps are nothing but
progression in pranayama. This means that when the prana stays in
the Sushumna for a certain time, it is called pratyahara; when it stays a
little longer, it is called dharana (concentration); even longer, it is
called dhyana (meditation); and for an even longer period, it is called
samadhi.   Samadhi is said to destroy death because you now
understand that you are not the body but the Immortal Self. Our goal
is this Ananda or Bliss. The Supreme Bliss of being absorbed in
Brahman is Sat-Chit-Ananda (Existence-Knowledge-Bliss Absolute),
or God. Just as a drop of water merges with the ocean and becomes
the ocean itself, so the individual merges with the Supreme.

Brahmananda's Commentary: *Destroying death means
enabling the yogi to shed his body at will. This is explained later on.*

*The bliss of a Jivanmukta is brought about when the mind is
stilled and the vasanas (karmic tendencies) are destroyed. This
bliss is that of Vedehamukti, when the prarabda karma is
exhausted, and a permanent union takes place between Jiva
and Parabrahman.*

राजयोग: समाधिश्च उन्मनी च मनोन्मनी।
अमरत्वं लयस्तत्त्वं शून्याशून्यं परं पदम्॥ ३॥

अमनस्कं तथाद्वैतं निरालम्बं निरञ्जनम्।
जीवन्मुक्तिश्च सहजा तुर्या चेत्येकवाचका:॥ ४॥

(3 & 4) Raja Yoga, Samadhi, Unmani, Manomani,
Amaratva (immortality), Laya (absorption), Tattva
(Truth), Shunyashunya (void and yet non-void),
Paramapada (the supreme state), Amanaska
(suspended operation of the mind), Advaita (non-
dual), Niralamba (without support), Niranjana
(pure), Jivanmukti (emancipated state while in the
body), Sahaja (natural state), and Turiya – all of
these mean the same thing.

Samadhi has various names, and these are the names.   Raja Yoga is
when the mind is still, without any waves. Samadhi is when the mind
doesn't function any more and you see your Self (Atman) clearly, or
when there is Oneness with Brahman.   Unmani is Hatha Yoga
samadhi; it refers to the state in which the prana and apana are united
and go the higher chakras. Manomani literally means "that which
brings joy to the mind," and the only thing which brings joy is the Self,
the Atman. Immortality refers to transcending the body so that you
identify with the Atman. Concentration is on the Atman: "I am that
Brahman." Shunyashunya means void and not void because in that
state there is no time, space or causation, but yet one feels pure
consciousness and awareness, extreme bliss and happiness.
Paramapada means the highest state. Amanaska comes from "manas,"
meaning mind, and "a" meaning not. When there is no mind, there is
no time, space, nor causation. Advaita, the non-dual state is also called
Asamprajnata samadhi. In the Niralamba state Atman or Brahman
has no support, it is everywhere, it supports everything. Niranjana is
pure Consciousness. Jivanmukti is the liberated state. Sahajavastha is
the natural state: Sat-Chit-Ananda. Turiya is the superconscious state.
All of these terms refer to the same thing.

सलिले सैन्धवं यद्वत्साम्यं भजति योगत:।
तथात्ममनसोरैक्यं   समाधिरभिधीयते ॥ ५ ॥

(5) *As a grain of salt thrown into the water unites and becomes one with it, a like union between the mind and the Atman is samadhi.*

Here again is another definition of samadhi. When salt is thrown into water, it becomes one with the water. In the same way, the mind and the soul are united so that at that time there is only oneness, or samadhi.

यदा सङ्क्षीयते प्राणो मानसं च प्रलीयते।
तदा समरसत्वं च   समाधिरभिधीयते ॥ ६ ॥

(6) *When the prana is without movement (in Kumbhaka) and the manas (mind) is annihilated (absorbed in the Self), the state of harmony then arising is called samadhi.*

That prana which creates the inhalation and exhalation, and the apana which goes to the sexual organs and which creates thoughts, are stopped, then the state which remains is your Self: "I Am." This also is called samadhi.

Brahmananda's Commentary: *This is the state of Samprajnata Samadhi described by Patanjali.*

तत्समं च द्वयोरैक्यं जीवात्मपरमात्मनो:।
प्रणष्टसर्वसङ्कल्प: समाधि: सोऽभिधीयते ॥ ७ ॥

(7) That state of equilibrium which is the union of Jivatman and Paramatman, in which there is the annihilation of all ideas, that is called Samadhi.

The Jivatman is the individual soul. It unites with the Supreme Brahman or Paramatman or God. When this union takes place, then we can truly say that "I and my Father are one." I is the individual; Father is the Supreme. That union is called samadhi.

Brahmananda's Commentary: *This is Asamprajnata Samadhi in which there is no distinction of knower, known or knowing.*

राजयोगस्य माहात्म्यं को वा जानाति तत्त्वतः।
ज्ञानं मुक्तिः स्थितिः सिद्धिर्गुरुवाक्येन लभ्यते ॥ ८ ॥

(8) He who really knows the greatness of Raja Yoga, obtains through the favor of the guru: jnana, mukti, sthiti, and siddhis.

When Raja yogis achieve full control over the mind, then they reach the Immortal State. Jnana is the direct cognition of one's own Atman as Parabrahman, mukti is vedeha mukti, sthiti is jivanmukti, and siddhis are anima, etc.

दुर्लभो विषयत्यागो दुर्लभं तत्त्वदर्शनम्।
दुर्लभा सहजावस्था सद्गुरोः करुणां विना ॥ ९ ॥

(9) Without the kind grace of the guru, and without indifference to worldly pleasures, the real cognition of the Truth and the natural state of Being (sahajavastha which is the supreme state) are most difficult to attain.

For the guru's grace one should have devotion. Without devotion, your own efforts in pranayama, etc. will not bring success because of the many obstacles. So the grace of God and of guru is very essential.

Indifference to worldly pleasures is vairagya (dispassion). This world is nothing but a mirage. As there is no true happiness, you want to find the eternal happiness which is within you (you are that happiness). Until you have that dispassion, you will not be able to put full effort behind your Yoga practice, so that eventually your vairagya will dissipate, causing you to go back into your old ruts: drinking, smoking, etc. Therefore you must truly realize that all this drinking and smoking will bring you pain and disease, and you must wish to escape from this. If you realize that you will have to be reincarnated to come back again and again to go through the same learning experiences, you will want to get out of this cycle. Then you will take Yoga seriously and you will have the energy to do this work.

विविधैरासनै: कुम्भैर्विचित्रै: करणैरपि।
प्रबुद्धायां महाशक्तौ प्राण: शून्ये प्रलीयते ॥ १० ॥

(10) When the great Power (Kundalini) has been roused by the various asanas, kumbhakas and mudras, the prana is quiescent in the void (Brahmarandhra).

Through asanas you are regulating the prana. Asanas divert the prana from one area to another, increase or reduce the vibratory level or charge specific areas. Asanas which apply pressure on the solar plexus increase the vibratory level. The lumbar region (lower back) is where the Kundalini Shakti resides. When we loosen those vertebrae so that the discs are no longer compressed, we reduce pressure on the physical nerves, and this in turn affects the astral nerves. Asanas are not just physical exercise. The purpose of all asanas is to reduce this blocked energy. Together with pranayama, bandhas, and mudras, you try to awaken the Kundalini, and when the prana goes in the Sushumna, this state is called Shunya, or vacuum. It is not a physical vacuum; it means that there is no time or space awareness.

उत्पन्नशक्तिबोधस्य त्यक्तनिःशेषकर्मणः ।
योगिनः सहजावस्था स्वयमेव प्रजायते ॥ ११ ॥

*(11) In the yogi, in whom the (Kundalini) Shakti is
awakened and who is free of all karmas, the truly natural
State (of samadhi) comes into being on its own.*

The purpose is not to force anything; it is a natural process. From
watering the plant, eventually you will get flowers and fruits. In the
same way, from asanas, pranayama, japa, etc., practiced regularly and
increased little by little, the Kundalini automatically awakens. There is
no fast or easy method; each individual has to find his own
evolutionary rate. Each river has its own level beyond which it will
overflow, or if its flow is too low, it will dry out before it reaches the
ocean. In the same way, you have to practice regularly and avoid too
much enthusiasm in the beginning. Try to find the middle path, then
eventually you will reach that state.

Brahmananda's Commentary: *In the practice of the asanas,
all physical acts come to an end, and the actions are confined to
prana, and the organs of sense. By Kumbhaka, the movement
of Prana and the sense organs is arrested and there remains the
mental activity. By pratyahara, dharana, dhyana and
samprajnyata samadhi, mental activity ceases and the actions
are confined only to the buddhi. By extreme vairagya (absence
of attachment) and long practice of samprajnyata samadhi, the
acts of the buddhi are abandoned and the yogi attains his
original unchangeable state, which is the final beatitude.*

सुषुम्नावाहिनि प्राणे शून्ये विशति मानसे ।
तदा सर्वाणि कर्माणि निर्मूलयति योगवित् ॥ १२ ॥

(12) When the prana moves in the Sushumna and the mind is absorbed in the Shunya (void), the intelligent yogi (he who can end the modifications of the mind) uproots all karma.

Brahmananda's Commentary: *"Void" means Brahman unaffected by time, space, or matter.*

अमराय नमस्तुभ्यं सोऽपि कालस्त्वया जित:।
पतितं   वदने   यस्य   जगदेतच्चराचरम्॥ १३॥

(13) Salutations to you Amaras (immortals), by whom time, into whose mouth the universe (movable and immovable) falls, has been conquered.

Svatmarama calls those yogis who have conquered time by bringing the Kundalini Shakti into the Sushumna, "Amaras," immortals. You are all immortal, but it is necessary to acquire that knowledge that you are no longer bound by time, space, causation, birth, death, change. This is the author's benediction, not to the body, but to the Higher Self, now realized.

Brahmananda's Commentary: *Here he addresses the siddhas using the term "immortals."*

चित्ते समत्वमापन्ने वायौ व्रजति मध्यमे।
तदाऽमरोली वज्रोली सहजोली प्रजायते॥ १४॥

(14) When the mind has reached a state of equanimity (or when it joins the Atman) and the prana moves through the Sushumna, then one obtains Amaroli, Vajroli and Sahajoli.

In time, the various mudras and bandhas come automatically.

Brahmananda's Commentary: *This stanza shows that Vajroli and the other like processes are not literally physical, but have a symbolic significance.*

ज्ञानं कुतो मनसि सम्भवतीह तावत्
पाणोऽपि जीवति मनो म्रियते न यावत्।
प्राणो मनो द्वयमिदं विलयं नयेद्यो-
मोक्षं स गच्छति नरो न कथञ्चिदन्यः॥ १५॥

(15) *How can jnana (spiritual knowledge) arise in the mind, as long as the prana lives (is active) and the mind is not dead (in abeyance)? He who causes both prana and mind to become quiescent obtains liberation. No other person can do so.*

Brahmananda's Commentary: *The prana lives so long as it flows through Ida and Pingala; the sense organs live so long as they seek objects; the mind lives so long as it is shaped by the various objects of perception. Prana dies when it remains without movement in Brahmarandhra. The mind dies when it is not modified by objects. In this stanza Yoga is said to be essential to Jnana. In the **Yogavijaya**, Parvati asks, "Some say that liberation is obtained through knowledge only, then what is the use of Yoga?" Siva replies, "A battle is won by a sword, but what is the use of a sword without a war and valor? So both are absolutely necessary." If it is argued that King Janaka and other great men did not practice Yoga at all, the answer is: kings like Janaka, Vaisyas like Tuladhara, Sudras like Pailavaka, women like Maitreyi, Sarngi, Dandili, Cadala have obtained knowledge without practicing Yoga, because they had perfected Yoga in their previous incarnations. We also hear that, by the force of Yoga practiced in previous lives, many attained the state of Brahma, sons of Brahma, devarishi, brahmarishi, muni and* *bhakta. They attained complete knowledge without being initiated by a guru. Hiranyagarbha (Brahma), Vasistha, Narada, Suka, Vamadeva and Sanatkumara are said to have been born Siddhas.*

Jnana is knowledge of the Atman (Self, or God). You cannot obtain God Realization or Self Realization unless prana is brought into the Sushumna. When only the Ida and Pingala are functioning, it is impossible to reach this state. Stopping the Ida and Pingala, and getting the prana into the Sushumna is the purpose of all Yogas. Without that you have knowledge only of the body and you identify with it. That is what the author means by saying "his prana lives." This state is called ajnana (non-knowledge); it is ignorance, "I am the body" is ignorance: "I am the Atman" is Knowledge.

When the prana and apana are withdrawn from the left and right sides and enter into the Sushumna, then the mind becomes extinct. This means that the mind is no longer operating in the ordinary sense. According to Hatha Yoga, moksha is obtained only by those people who are able to practice this.

ज्ञात्वा सुषुम्नासद्भेदं कृत्वा वायुं च मध्यगम्।
स्थित्वा सदैव सुस्थाने ब्रह्मरन्ध्रे निरोधयेत्॥ १६॥

(16) Having known the secret of finding the way into the Sushumna and forcing the prana into it, the yogi should then, seating himself in a convenient spot, restrain his prana in the Brahmarandhra.

Brahmananda's Commentary: *The "convenient spot" is described in Chapter I. verse 12.*

सूर्याचन्द्रमसौ धत्तः कालं रात्रिंदिवात्मकम्।
भोक्त्री सुषुम्ना कालस्य गुह्यमेतदुदाहृतम्॥ १७॥

(17) *The Sun and the Moon are said to regulate day and night. Sushumna is said to swallow time. This is a secret.*

Brahmananda's Commentary: *The prana moves in the Ida (Moon) for about one hour, and then in the Pingala (Sun). So two hours form a day and night for the yogi. The ordinary day consists of twelve such days. When the prana leaves Ida and Pingala and remains in the Sushumna, then there is no time. So Sushumna is said to swallow time. The yogi, knowing beforehand the time of his death, takes his prana to Brahmarandhra and defies time (death) and discards his body at will.*

द्वासप्ततिसहस्राणि   नाडीद्वाराणि   पञ्जरे।
सुषुम्ना शाम्भवी शक्ति: शेषास्त्वेव निरर्थका:॥ १८॥

(18) *There are 72,000 nadis in this cage (the body). (Of these) Sushumna is the middle nadi, containing the Shambhavi Shakti, which possesses the virtue of giving delight to the yogis. The others (Ida, Pingala, etc.) are not of great use.*

वायु: परिचितो यस्मादग्निना सह कुण्डलीम्।
बोधयित्वा   सुषुम्नायां   प्रविशेदनिरोधत:॥ १९॥

(19) *He who is the master of the restraint of breath, having brightened up his gastric fire, should awake the Kundalini and make it enter the Sushumna without any restriction.*

सुषुम्नावाहिनि प्राणे सिद्ध्यत्येव मनोन्मनी।
अन्यथात्वितराभ्यासाः प्रयासायैव योगिनाम्॥ २०॥

*(20) When the prana flows through the Sushumna,
the Manomani state comes of itself. Other means are
mere useless endeavors on the part of a yogi.*

पवनो बध्यते येन मनस्तेनैव बध्यते।
मनश्च बध्यते येन पवनस्तेन बध्यते॥ २१॥

*(21) He who suspends (restrains) the breath,
restrains also the working of the mind. He who has
controlled the mind, has also controlled the breath.*

पवनो बध्यते येन मनस्तेनैव बध्यते।
मनश्च बध्यते येन पवनस्तेन बध्यते॥ २१॥

*(22) The (activity of the) mind is made active by two
things: the prana and the vasanas (karmic affinities).
When one of these dies, the other comes to an end also.*

मनो यत्र विलीयेत पवनस्तत्र लीयते।
पवनो लीयते यत्र मनस्तत्र विलीयते॥ २३॥

*(23) Where the mind is absorbed, there the prana is
restrained; and where the prana is restrained, there
the mind is quiescent.*

दुग्धाम्बुवत् सम्मिलितावुभौ तौ तुल्यक्रियौ मानसमारुतौ हि ।
यतो   मरुत्तत्र   मन: प्रवृत्तिर्यतो   मनस्तत्र   मरुत्प्रवृत्ति:॥ २४॥

*(24) Mind and prana have affinity for each other
like milk and water. If one is restrained, the other is
restrained also. In whatever place (chakra) the
prana is restrained, there the mind becomes fixed.
Where the mind is fixed, there the prana is restrained.*

तत्रैकनाशादपरस्य   नाश   एकप्रवृत्तेरपरप्रवृत्ति: ।
अध्वस्तयोश्चेन्द्रियवर्गवृत्ति: प्रध्वस्तयोर्मोक्षपदस्य सिद्धि:॥ २५ ॥

*(25) If one is suspended, the other is also set at
rest. If one acts, the other also does the same. If
they are not stopped, all the indriyas (the senses)
keep actively engaged in their respective work. If the
mind and prana are stopped, the state of
emancipation is attained.*

रसस्य   मनसश्चैव   चञ्चलत्वं   स्वभावत: ।
रसो बद्धो मनो बद्धं किं न सिद्ध्यति भूतले॥ २६ ॥

*(26)   The nature of the mind and mercury are
unsteady or fluctuating. If they are bound, i.e. made
firm, what is impossible on the face of this earth?*

मूर्च्छितो हरते व्याधीन् मृतो जीवयति स्वयम्।
बद्ध: खेचरतां धत्ते रसो वायुश्च पार्वति॥ २७॥

*(27)   O Parvati! Mercury, reduced to a solid form by
the help of herbs, and prana, brought to a quiet state
by kumbhaka, destroy all diseases. When they
themselves are so destroyed cause sick persons to live
long, and also enable persons to rise in the air.*

Brahmananda's Commentary: *Mercury is made solid and
inactive by a certain process. In the same way, the prana is
stopped when absorbed in the Brahmarandhra by means of
rechaka and kumbhaka.*

*When mercury is bound (by a certain process) and reduced to
the form of a pill, it is called gahanagutika. And by putting it
in the mouth [not to be taken literally], one can rise in the air.
In the same manner, the prana, when taken to the center
between the two eyebrows, enables one to rise in the air. The
Goraksha Shataka says, "Between the eyebrows there appears a
round spot, black as a ball of collyrium. It is the essence of Vayu,
and its presiding deity is Ishwara. Restraining the prana in this
chakra, along with the mind, for two hours, gives to a yogi the
power of rising in the air."*

मन: स्थैर्य स्थिरो वायुस्ततो बिन्दु: स्थिरो भवेत्।
बिन्दुस्थैर्यात् सदा सच्चं पिण्डस्थैर्य प्रजायते॥ २८॥

*(28) When the mind is firm, the prana is also firm,
and hence is the stability of semen which secures
strength and makes the body strong and healthy.*

इन्द्रियाणां मनो नाथो मनोनाथस्तु मारुत:।
मारुतस्य लयो नाथ: स लयो नादमाश्रित: ॥ २९ ॥

(29) The mind is the lord of indriyas (the organs of senses). Prana is the lord of the mind. Laya (or absorption) is the lord of the prana, and that laya depends on the nada (the inner sounds).

सोऽयमेवास्तु मोक्षाख्यो मास्तु वापि मतान्तरे।
मन: प्राणलये कश्चिदानन्द: सम्प्रवर्तते ॥ ३० ॥

(30) This itself (the quiescence of the mind) may be called moksha, though others say that it is not. However, when the prana and the manas have been absorbed, an indefinable joy ensues.

प्रणष्टश्वासनिश्वास: प्रध्वस्तविषयग्रह:।
निश्चेष्टो निर्विकारश्च लयो जयति योगिनाम् ॥ ३१ ॥

(31) A yogi who has suspended his inspirations and expirations, whose senses have become inactive or insensible, whose mental activity has ceased, and whose emotions of the mind have become quiet, obtains success in Laya Yoga.

उच्छित्रसर्वसङ्कल्पो   नि:शेषाशेषचेष्टित:।
स्वावगम्यो लय: कोऽपि जायते वागगोचर:॥ ३२॥

*(32) When the mental and physical activities have
entirely ceased, the indescribable state of laya
ensues, which is known by the Self, but is beyond the
reach of words.*

यत्र   दृष्टिर्लयस्तत्र   भूतेन्द्रियसनातनी।
सा शक्तिर्जीवभूतानां द्वे अलक्ष्ये लयं गते॥ ३३॥

*(33) When the drusthi (mental perception) is
directed, there (in Brahman) is absorption. That
(avidya) in which eternally exist the five elements
(such as earth) and the ten indriyas, and that force
(shakti) which is in all living beings, both are
dissolved in the characteristicless (Brahman).*

लयो लय इति प्राहु: कीदृशं लयलक्षणम्।
अपुनर्वासनोत्थानाल्लयो विषयविस्मृति:॥ ३४॥

*(34) People say "laya, laya," but what is the nature
of laya? Laya is the non-recollection of the objects of
the senses due to the non-recurrence of previously
acquired impressions and tendencies (vasanas).*

वेदशास्त्रपुराणानि सामान्यगणिका इव।
एकैव शाम्भवी मुद्रा गुप्ता कुलवधूरिव॥ ३५॥

*(35) The Vedas, shastras and puranas are like common
prostitutes (as they are available to all men). But
Shambhavi mudra is like a respectable woman,
zealously guarded and approached by only a few.*

अन्तर्लक्ष्यं बहिर्दृष्टिर्निमेषोन्मेषवर्जिता।
एषा सा शाम्भवी मुद्रा वेदशास्त्रेषु गोपिता॥ ३६॥

*(36) Shambhavi mudra consists in fixing the mind
internally (in any chakra from the Muladhara to the
Brahmarandhra), and in fixing the eyes upon some
external object without winking. (When the mind is
absorbed in the object contemplated upon, the eyes
do not wink). This mudra is kept secret in the Vedas
and the shastras.*

अन्तर्लक्ष्यविलीनचित्तपवनो योगी यदा वर्तते।
दृष्ट्या निश्चलतारया बहिरध: पश्यन्नपश्यन्नपि।
मुद्रेयं खलुशाम्भवी भवति सा लब्धा प्रसादाद् गुरो:।
शून्याशून्यविलक्षणं स्फुरति तत्तत्त्वं पदं शाम्भवम्॥ ३७॥

*(37) When the yogi remains with the mind and
breath absorbed in the internal object, when the
pupils (of his eyes) are motionless. Though his eyes*

perceive without, he sees not, i.e. does not grasp the objects, it is indeed called the Shambhavi mudra. When this state is obtained by the favor of the guru, the yogi realizes the state of Shambhu, which is resplendent and which is beyond Shunyashunya (void and yet not void).

Brahmananda's Commentary: *The attention should be directed to the Anahata chakra and to contemplation upon Iswara (personal god, with attributes) or upon Brahman, which is the real object of the two sentences: "That Thou Art" (Tat Twam Asi), and "I am Brahman" (Aham Brahmasmi). It is beyond the void because, being absorbed in the object contemplated upon, it becomes of the nature of Sat (existence). It is also beyond non-void because even this conception ceases afterwards.*

श्री शाम्भव्याश्च खेचर्या अवस्थाधामभेदतः।
भवेच्चित्तलयानन्दः शून्ये चित्सुखरूपिणि॥ ३८॥

(38) The Shambhavi and Khechari mudras, though apparently differing in the position of the eyes and places to which attention or mind is directed, are one in their result. Both of them bring about the state of Bliss, Absolute Consciousness, caused by the mind being absorbed in the Atman, which is void.

Brahmananda's Commentary: *It is called void because it is not affected by time, place or matter. It has nothing like itself, and yet nothing different from itself. The states of the two mudras are said to be different because, in Shambhavi mudra the eyes are directed towards some external object. The places* *are different because in Shambhavi mudra the attention is fixed on the Anahata chakra, and in Khechari mudra between the eyebrows.*

तारे ज्योतिषिसंयोज्य किञ्चिदुन्नमयेद्भ्रुवौ ।
पूर्वयोगं मनो युञ्जन्नुन्मनीकारक: क्षणात् ॥ ३९ ॥

(39) *Direct the pupils (of the eyes) towards the light by raising the eyebrows a little upwards. Assume the position laid down for Shambhavi mudra. This brings on Unmani avastha.*

केचिदागमजालेन   केचिन्निगमसङ्कुलै: ।
केचित्तर्केण मुह्यन्ति नैव जानन्ति तारकम् ॥ ४० ॥

(40) *Some confuse themselves by the enticing promises of the shastras and the tantras, some by the vedic-karmas, and others by logic; but none of them knows the value of the Unmani avastha that enables one to cross the ocean of existence.*

अर्धोन्मीलितलोचन: स्थिरमना नासाग्रदत्तेक्षण-
        श्चन्द्रकोवपि लीनतामुपनयन्निस्पन्दभावेन य: ।
ज्योतीरूपमशेषबीजमखिलं देदीप्यमानं परं,
        तत्त्वं तत्पदमेति वस्तु परमं वाच्यं किमत्राधिकम् ॥ ४१ ॥

(41) *With half-closed eyes fixed on the tip of the nose, with a firm mind, and with the sun and the moon reduced to the state of suspension (by directing the prana from Ida and Pingala, and forcing it into Sushumna), the yogi attains that state wherein he experiences the Truth in the form of resplendent light (jyoti), which is the source of all things, and which is the most supreme object to be gained. What else higher than this could be expected?*

Brahmananda's Commentary: Vasistha says, "When the eyes are directed to the tip of the nose or about 12 fingers from it, a clear firmament (akasha) appears and the fluctuations of prana cease."

दिवा न पूजयेल्लिङ्गं रात्रौ चैव न पूजयेत्।
सर्वदा पूजयेल्लिङ्गं दिवारात्रिनिरोधतः॥ ४२॥

(42) *Do not worship the linga during the day nor during the night. Avoiding the night and the day, he should always worship it.*

Brahmananda's Commentary: *"Linga" here means the Atman. It is day when the prana flows through the sun (Pingala), and it is night when it flows through the moon (Ida). One should not contemplate upon the Atman when the prana is flowing through either of them. One should stop the course of prana through the Ida or Pingala, and make it flow through the Sushumna when contemplating upon the Atman.*

सव्यदक्षिणनाडीस्थो मध्ये चरति मारुत:।
तिष्ठते खेचरी मुद्रा तस्मिन्स्थाने न संशय:॥ ४३॥

*(43) When the prana which naturally flows through
the right and the left nadis, is in the middle of the
two eyebrows (Sushumna), the Khechari mudra
becomes perfect. There is no doubt about this.*

इडापिङ्गलयोर्मध्ये शून्यं चैवानिलं ग्रसेत्।
तिष्ठते खेचरी मुद्रा तत्र सत्यं पुन: पुन:॥ ४४॥

*(44) If the Pranavayu, which gives birth to the
Shunya (Sushumna nadi) existing between the Ida
and Pingala, be swallowed up, Khechari mudra
becomes steady in the Sushumna nadi. No doubt,
this is the correct method.*

Brahmananda's Commentary: *"Swallowing" the breath
means that the prana should be made to remain firm in
the Sushumna.*

सूर्याचन्द्रमसोर्मध्ये निरालम्बान्तरे पुन:।
संस्थिता व्योमचक्रे या सा मुद्रा नाम खेचरी॥ ४५॥

*(45) Again, between the Ida and Pingala, exists an
unsupported (niralamba) collection of akasha chakras.
The mudra practiced in it is called Khechari mudra.*

सोमाद्यत्रोदिता धारा साक्षात्सा शिववल्लभा ।
पूरयेदतुलां दिव्यां सुषुम्नां पश्चिमे मुखे ॥ ४६ ॥

*(46) The Khechari mudra in which the stream of
nectar flows from the moon, is very much liked by the
God Siva. The Sushumna, having no equal (in
greatness), is the best of the nadis which must be
stopped by the tongue turned upward into the roof of
the palate.*

पुरस्ताच्चैव पूर्येत निश्चिता खेचरी भवेत् ।
अभ्यस्ता खेचरी मुद्राप्युन्मनी समप्रजायते ॥ ४७ ॥

*(47) If the Sushumna is stopped previously from
without by the suspension of the prana, it perfects the
Khechari mudra. By frequent practice of the mudra,
the Unmani (Turiya Avastha) naturally follows.*

Brahmananda's Commentary: *If the Sushumna be not
stopped from without at the time of practice, it leads to the state
of ignorance, for it does not produce a perfect Khechari mudra.*

भ्रवोर्मध्ये शिवस्थानं मनस्तत्र विलीयते ।
ज्ञातव्यं तत्पदं तुर्यं तत्र कालो न विद्यते ॥ ४८ ॥

(48) *Between the eyebrows is the seat of Siva, wherein the mind becomes absorbed. This is known as the Turiya (fourth state of consciousness beyond the waking, dream and deep sleep states). Death (Time) is not experienced by the practicer of this mudra.*

अभ्यसेत् खेचरीं तावद्यावत्स्याद्योगनिद्रित: ।
सम्प्राप्तयोगनिद्रस्य कालो नास्ति कदाचन ॥ ४९ ॥

(49) *One should practice Khechari mudra until he gets into the Yoga sleep (samadhi). One who is in this sleep, Time (Death) does not exist.*

निरालम्बं मन: कृत्वा न किञ्चिदपि चिन्तयेत् ।
स बाह्याभ्यन्तरे व्योम्नि घटवत्तिष्ठति ध्रुवम् ॥ ५० ॥

(50) *After making the mind supportless (by removing it from every object of conception), he should not think of anything. He certainly then remains like a pot filled inside and outside with akasha.*

बाह्यवायुर्यथा लीनस्तथा मध्यो न संशय: ।
स्वस्थाने स्थिरतामेति पवनो मनसा सह ॥ ५१ ॥

(51) *When the breath from without ceases, the breath within the body also becomes absorbed. There is no doubt about it. After this, the prana, along with the mind, becomes steady in the Brahmarandhra.*

एवमभ्यस्यतस्तस्य वायुमार्गे दिवानिशम् ।
अभ्यासाज्जीर्यते वायुर्मनस्तत्रैव लीयते ॥ ५२ ॥

*(52) By thus practicing restraint of prana in the
Sushumna night and day, where the prana through
practice is absorbed, there the mind is also absorbed.*

अमृतैः प्लावयेद्देहमापादतलमस्तकम् ।
सिद्ध्यत्येव महाकायो महाबलपराक्रमः ॥ ५३ ॥

*(53) One should saturate the body from the head to
the foot with the stream of nectar (flowing from the
Moon). He then becomes endowed with an excellent
body, great strength, and valor. Thus the Khecari has
been described.*

शक्तिमध्ये मनः कृत्वा शक्तिं मानसमध्यगाम् ।
मनसा मन आलोक्य धारयेत्परमं पदम् ॥ ५४ ॥

*(54) Placing the mind in the Shakti (Kundalini),
and holding the Shakti in the center of the mind; by
means of contemplation, unite them together. And
exciting the Shakti, look at the mind with the
antahkarana, and make the Supreme state the object
of dhyana.*

Brahmananda's Commentary: *The meaning seems to be this: by taking the prana and the mind to the Brahmarandhra and contemplating on Kundalini (Shakti), the mind and the Kundalini are absorbed into one another. Looking upon manas with the antahkarana means contemplating upon buddhi with the manas.*

खमध्ये कुरु चात्मानमात्ममध्ये च खं कुरु।
सर्वं च खमयं कृत्वा न किञ्चिदपि चिन्तयेत्॥ ५५ ॥

(55) Place Atman in the midst of the akasha, and the akasha in the midst of the Atman. And on reducing everything to the form of akasha, one must not think of anything else.

Brahmananda's Commentary: *The Akasha means Brahman, into which one must make his Atman united by constantly thinking himself to be Brahman, and then abandon all thoughts of the objective and subjective nature.*

अन्तः शून्योबहिः शून्यः शून्यः कुम्भ इवाम्बरे।
अन्तः पूर्णो बहिः पूर्णः पूर्णः कुम्भ इवार्णवे ॥ ५६ ॥

(56) (The yogi in samadhi) is void within and without, like a pot in the Akasha. He is also like a pot in the ocean, full within and without.

Brahmananda's Commentary: *He is void within and without because the antahkarana has become insensible of itself and the surrounding nature. It is also full, because it has become Brahman itself within and without.*

बाह्यचिन्ता न कर्त्तव्या तथैवान्तरचिन्तनम्।
सर्वचिन्तां परित्यज्य न किञ्चिदपि चिन्तयेत्॥ ५७॥

(57) He should think of nothing in the outside nature. So also, he should give up personal thoughts. He should abandon all thoughts subjective and objective.

संकल्पमात्रकलनैव जगत्समग्रं
संकल्पमात्रकलनैव मनोविलास:।
संकल्पमात्रमतिमुत्सृज निर्विकल्प-
माश्रित्यनिश्चयमवाप्नुहि राम शान्तिम्॥ ५८॥

(58) The external universe is created by our thoughts, as also the imaginary world. Having abandoned the idea of permanency in these creations of thought, and concentrating your mind upon that which is not subject to any changes, O Rama, obtain everlasting and certain Peace.

Brahmananda's Commentary: *This is taken from the Yoga Vasistha. Brahman is free from the conceptions of the actor and enjoyer. It is without a second. Nothing exists without it, and nothing proceeds from it. It is not affected by time, space and matter. It is therefore free from any change.*

कर्पूरमनले यद्वत्सैन्धवं सलिले   यथा।
तथा सन्धीयमानं च मनस्तत्त्वे विलीयते॥ ५९॥

(59) The mind when concentrated (on the Atman), becomes one with it, like camphor with the flame and like salt with the water of the ocean, the mind dissolved in contact with Reality.

ज्ञेयं सर्वं प्रतीतं च ज्ञानं च मन उच्यते।
ज्ञानं ज्ञेयं समं नष्टं नान्य: पन्था द्वितीयक:॥ ६० ॥

(60) Everything that is seen and experienced is called "the known," and the faculty of knowing is called the mind. When the known and the knowledge are lost, there is no duality.

मनोदृश्यमिदं सर्वं यत्किञ्चित्सचराचरम्।
मनसो ह्युन्मनीभावाद् द्वैतं नैवोपलभ्यते॥ ६१ ॥

(61) Both animate and inanimate things in the universe are perceived by the mind. When the mind is lost in the Unmani (Turiya) state, then duality does not exist.

ज्ञेयवस्तुपरित्यागाद् विलयं याति मानसम्।
मनसो विलये जाते कैवल्यमवशिष्यते॥ ६२ ॥

(62) As all the objects of perception are abandoned, the mind becomes of the nature of Satchidananda. When the mind is reduced to this state, then the kaivalya (absoluteness) remains: the yogi becomes of the nature of the non-dual Atman.

एवं नानाविधोपायाः सम्यक्स्वानुभवान्विताः।
समाधिमार्गाः कथिताः पूर्वाचार्यैर्महात्मभिः॥ ६३॥

*(63) These are the various means for attaining
samadhi, described by the great ancient teachers from
their own experience.*

सुषुम्नायै कुण्डलिन्यै सुधायै चन्द्रजन्मने।
मनोन्मन्यै नमस्तुभ्यं महाशक्त्यै चिदात्मने॥ ६४॥

*(64) Salutations to the Sushumna, to the Kundalini,
to the stream of nectar flowing from the moon to the
Mamomani (Turiya Avashta), and to the great Power
in the form of pure consciousness (Chit Shakti).*

अशक्यतत्त्वबोधानां मूढानामपि सम्मतम्।
प्रोक्तं गोरक्षनाथेन नादोपासनमुच्यते॥ ६५॥

*(65) Now I begin to describe the practice of nada
(anahata or unstruck sounds) that has been given
out by Gorakshanatha, and which has been accepted
even by those who are unable to realize the truth,
and who have not studied the shastras.*

श्री आदिनाथेन सपादकोटिलयप्रकाराः कथिता जयन्ति।
नादानुसन्धानकमेकमेव मन्यामहे मुख्यतमं लयानाम्॥ ६६॥

(66) The Adinatha (Lord Siva) has given out a one crore and a quarter (1,25,00,000) of ways for the attainment of laya, but I think that the practice of nada is the best of them all.

मुक्तासने स्थितो योगी मुद्रां सन्धाय शाम्भवीम् ।
शृणुयाद्दक्षिणे   कर्णे   नादमन्तःस्थमेकधीः ॥ ६७ ॥

(67) The yogi, sitting in the Muktasana posture, and assuming the Shambhavi mudra, should listen with a concentrated mind to the sounds within. These are heard in the right ear.

Brahmananda's Commentary: *These sounds proceed from the Sushumna. They are of ten sorts: buzzing, the sound of a flute, bells, waves, thunder, falling rain, etc.*

श्रवणपुटनयनयुगलघ्राणमुखानां निरोधनं कार्यम् ।
शुद्धसुषुम्नासरणौ   स्फुटममलः   श्रूयते   नादः ॥ ६८ ॥

(68) Close the ears, the nose, the mouth, and the eyes. Then a clear sound is heard distinctly in the Sushumna (which has been purified by pranayama).

Brahmananda's Commentary: *The ears are to be closed with the thumbs of both hands, the eyes with the forefingers, the nose with the middle fingers, and the mouth with the rest. This is called Shanmukhi mudra.*

आरम्भश्च घटश्चैव तथा परिचयोऽपि च।
निष्पत्ति: सर्वयोगेषु स्यादवस्थाचतुष्टयम्॥ ६९ ॥

*(69) In all the yogic practices there are four
stages: arambha, ghata, parichaya, and nishpatti.*

ब्रह्मग्रन्थेर्भवेद् भेदो ह्यानन्द: शून्यसम्भव:।
विचित्र: क्वणको देहेऽनाहत: श्रूयते ध्वनि:॥ ७० ॥

*(70) In the first stage (Arambha Avastha), when
the Brahma granthi (knot of Brahma that is in the
Anahata chakra) is pierced (by pranayama), there is
the bliss arising from the void (shunya or akasha of
the heart). The various sweet tinkling sounds (as of
ornaments) and the unstruck sound arising from the
akasha in the heart, are heard in the Anahata chakra
that is in the middle of the body.*

दिव्यदेहश्च तेजस्वी दिव्यगन्धस्त्वरोगवान्।
सम्पूर्णहृदय: शून्य आरम्भे योगवान् भवेत्॥ ७१ ॥

*(71) When the sound begins to be heard in the Shunya
(akasha), the yogi, possessed of a body resplendent and
giving out sweet odor, is free from all diseases, and his
heart is filled (with prana and bliss).*

Brahmananda's Commentary: *The akasha of the Anahata chakra (heart) is called Sunya; that of the Visuddha chakra (throat) is known as Atisunya; and that of the Ajna chakra (forehead) is Mahasunya.*

द्वितीयायां घटीकृत्य वायुर्भवति मध्यगः।
दृढासनो भवेद् योगी ज्ञानी देवसमस्तदा॥ ७२॥

(72) In the second stage (Ghata Avashta), the prana becomes one (with apana, and bindu) and enters the middle chakra. The yogi then becomes firm in the asanas, his intellect becomes more keen, and be becomes equal with the devas.

Brahmananda's Commentary: *In this stage, the prana and apana, the nada and bindu, the Jivatman and Paramatman are united. The middle chakra is the Vishuddha chakra in the throat.*

विष्णुग्रन्थेस्ततो भेदात् परमानन्दसूचकः।
अतिशून्ये विमर्दश्च भेरीशब्दस्तथा भवेत्॥ ७३॥

(73) When the Vishnu granthi, which is in the throat, is pierced (by the prana in kumbhaka), it is a sign that the Supreme Bliss is about to follow. In the Atishunya, which is the name of the space in the throat, a medley of rumbling sounds are heard like the sound of a kettledrum.

तृतीयायां तु विज्ञेयो विहायोमर्दलध्वनि: ।
महाशून्यं तदायाति सर्वसिद्धिसमाश्रयम् ॥ ७४ ॥

*(74) In the third stage (Parichaya Avastha), a
sound like that of a mardala (a kind of drum) is
heard in the akasha lying between the eyebrows. The
vayu (the prana) goes to the Maha shunya, which is
the seat of all siddhis.*

चित्तानन्दं तदा जित्वा सहजानन्दसम्भव: ।
दोषदु:खजराव्याधिक्षुधानिद्राविवर्जित: ॥ ७५ ॥

*(75) Having overcome the blissful state of the mind
(arising from the hearing of the sounds), he
experiences the natural state of bliss arising from a
realization of his Atman. He then becomes free from
all faults, pains, old age, diseases, hunger, and sleep.*

रुद्रग्रन्थिं यदा भित्त्वा   शर्वपीठगतोऽनिल: ।
निष्पत्तौ वैणव: शब्द: क्वणद्वीणाक्वणो भवेत् ॥ ७६ ॥

*(76) The prana, having forced the Rudra granthi
existing at the Ajna chakra, goes to the seat of
Ishwara. Then the fourth stage (Nishpatti) sets in,
wherein are heard the sounds of flute and veena.*

Brahmananda's Commentary: *The Nishpatti stage sets in
when the prana goes to the Brahmarandhra.*

एकीभूतं तदा चित्तं राजयोगाभिधानकम् ।
सृष्टिसंहारकर्त्तासौ योगीश्वरसमो भवेत् ॥ ७७ ॥

(77) When the mind becomes one (with the object concentrated upon), it is called Raja Yoga. The yogi, being the master of creation and destruction, becomes the equal of Ishwara.

Brahmananda's Commentary: *This means that he is the master of the disintegration and reintegration of matter, and hence can evolve forms and destroy them. Thus he performs, on a smaller scale, the functions of Ishwara.*

अस्तु वा मास्तु वा मुक्तिरत्रैवाखण्डितं सुखम् ।
लयोद्भवमिदं   सौख्यं   राजयोगादवाप्यते ॥ ७८ ॥

(78) Let there be mukti or not, here is uninterrupted Bliss. The bliss arising from laya is obtained only from the practice of Raja Yoga.

राजयोगमजानन्त: केवलं हठकर्मिण: ।
एतानभ्यासिनो मन्ये प्रयासफलवर्जितान् ॥ ७९ ॥

(79) There are many who are merely Hatha Yogis without the knowledge of Raja Yoga. I think them to be simply practitioners who do not get the fruit of their efforts.

उन्मन्यवाप्तये शीघ्रं भ्रू ध्यानं मम सम्मतम्।
राजयोगपदं प्राप्तुं सुखोपायोऽल्पचेतसाम्।
सद्य: प्रत्ययसन्धायी जायते नादजो लय:॥ ८० ॥

(80) I think that contemplation on the space between the eyebrows is the best way for the attainment of the Unmani (Turiya) avashta in a short time. For people of intellect, this is a suitable means for attaining Raja Yoga. The laya state arising from nada gives immediate experience.

Brahmananda's Commentary: *The results being soon perceptible are very convincing.*

नादानुसन्धानसमाधिभाजां योगीश्वराणां हृदि वर्धमानम्।
आनन्दमेकं वचसामगम्यं जानाति तं श्रीगुरुनाथ एक:॥ ८१ ॥

(81) Great yogis who practice samadhi through the concentration on nada, experience a joy arising in their hearts that surpasses all description, and which only the Sri Gurunath is able to know.

कर्णौ पिधाय हस्ताभ्यां यं शृणोति ध्वनिं मुनि:।
तत्र चित्तं स्थिरीकुर्याद्यावत्स्थिरपदं व्रजेत्॥ ८२ ॥

(82) The contemplative man (the muni), having closed his ears with his fingers, should fix his attention on the (anahata) sound that is heard within, until he attains the Turiya stage.

अभ्यस्यमानो नादोऽयं बाह्यमावृणुते ध्वनिम्।
पक्षाद्विक्षेपमखिलं जित्वा योगी सुखी भवेत्॥ ८३॥

*(83) The hearing of the sound thus practiced,
gradually overpowers and drowns out the external
sounds. The yogi, overcoming the instability of his
mind will, in fifteen days, become happy.*

श्रूयते प्रथमाभ्यासे नादो नानाविधो महान्।
ततोऽभ्यासे वर्धमाने श्रूयते सूक्ष्मसूक्ष्मक:॥ ८४॥

*(84) During the initial stages of the practice,
various prominent, inner sounds are heard. But when
progress is made, they become more and more subtle.*

आदौ   जलधिजीमूतभेरीझर्झरसम्भवा:।
मध्ये मर्दलशङ्खोत्था घण्टाकाहलजास्तथा॥ ८५॥

*(85) In the beginning, the sounds resemble those of
the ocean, the clouds, the kettledrum, and zarzara (a
sort of drum-cymbal). In the middle they resemble
those arising from the mardala, the conch, the bell,
and the horn.*

अन्ते तु किङ्क्रिणीवंशवीणाभ्रमर नि:स्वना:।
इति नानाविधा नादा: श्रूयन्ते देहमध्यगा:॥ ८६॥

(86) In the end they resemble those of the tinkling bells, the flutes, the veena, and the bees. Thus are heard the various sounds from the middle of the body.

महति श्रूयमाणेऽपि मेघभेर्यादिके ध्वनौ।
यत्र सूक्ष्मात्सूक्ष्मतरं नादमेव परामृशेत्॥ ८७॥

(87) Even when the loud sounds of the clouds and the kettledrum are heard, he should try to fix his attention on the subtler sounds.

घनमुत्सृज्य वा सूक्ष्मे सूक्ष्ममुत्सृज्य वा घने।
रममाणमपि क्षिप्तं मनो नान्यत्र चालयेत्॥ ८८॥

(88) He may change his attention from the loud to the subtle sounds, but he should never allow his attention to wander to other extraneous objects.

यत्र कुत्रापि वा नादे लगति प्रथमं मनः।
तत्रैव सुस्थिरीभूय तेन सार्धं विलीयते॥ ८९॥

(89) The mind fixes itself upon the nada, to which it is first attracted, until it becomes one with it.

Brahmananda's Commentary: *Stanzas 87, 88, and 89 gradually describe pratyahara, dharana, dhyana, and samadhi.*

मकरन्दं पिबन् भृङ्गो गन्धं नापेक्षते यथा।
नादासक्तं तथा चित्तं विषयान्न हि काङ्क्षते ॥ ९० ॥

*(90) As a bee, through drinking honey of flowers,
cares not for the odor, so the mind absorbed in the
nada does not care for the objects of enjoyment.*

मनो मत्तगजेन्द्रस्य विषयोद्यानचारिण:।
नियन्त्रणे समर्थोऽयं निनादनिशिताङ्कुश: ॥ ९१ ॥

*(91) The sharp iron goad of nada can effectively
curb the mind resembling that of a mad elephant
that wanders in the pleasant garden of the objects
of the senses.*

Brahmananda's Commentary: *Here is taught pratyahara by
drawing the mind away from the objects of the senses.*

बद्धं तु नादबन्धेन मन: संत्यक्तचापलम्।
प्रयाति सुतरां स्थैर्यं छिन्नपक्ष: खगो यथा ॥ ९२ ॥

*(92) When the mind, divested of its flighty nature
(caused by its constant identification with sense
objects), is bound by the cords of nada, it attains a
state of extreme concentration and remains quiet as a
bird that has lost its wings.*

Brahmananda's Commentary: *Having conquered the prana by pranayama, and the indriyas by pratyahara, he should concentrate his mind on God. Thus dharana is known by the concentration of the mind on a particular object.*

सर्वचिन्तां परित्यज्य सावधानेन चेतसा।
नाद एवानुसन्धेयो योगसाम्राज्यमिच्छता॥ ९३॥

(93) The yogi, desirous of obtaining the sovereignty of Yoga, should abandon all thoughts, and with a carefully concentrated mind, practice the nada laya.

Brahmananda's Commentary: *That is, his mind becomes one with the nada which represents the stage of dhyana.*

नादोऽन्तरङ्गसारङ्गबन्धने वागुरायते।
अन्तरङ्गकुरङ्गस्य वधे व्याधायतेऽपि च॥ ९४॥

(94) Nada is like a snare for catching the deer within, i.e. the mind. It is also the hunter who kills the deer (the mind).

Brahmananda's Commentary: *Like the hunter, nada first attracts the mind, binds it, and then kills it. It puts an end to the natural unsteadiness of the mind, and then absorbs it into itself.*

अन्तरङ्गस्य यमिनो वाजिनः परिघायते।
नादोपास्तिरतो नित्यमवधार्या हि योगिना॥ ९५॥

(95) Nada is like the bolt of a stable that prevents a horse (i.e. the mind of a yogi) from wandering. A yogi therefore, should daily practice concentration upon the nada.

बद्धं विमुक्तचाञ्चल्यं नादगन्धकजारणात् ।
मन: पारदमाप्नोति निरालम्बाख्यखेऽटनम् ॥ ९६ ॥

(96) Mercury, calcinated by the action of sulphur, becomes solid and divested of its active nature and enables it to rise in the air. So the mind is made steady by the action of the nada, which makes it unite in Brahman, which is all-pervading.

Brahmananda's Commentary: See stanza IV, 27 and commentary.

नादश्रवणत: क्षिप्रमन्तरङ्गभुजङ्गम: ।
विस्मृत्य सर्वमेकाग्र: कुत्रचिन्न हि धावति ॥ ९७ ॥

(97) The mind is like a serpent within, which on hearing the musical sound, becomes oblivious to all else and absorbed in the one thing, does not run away.

Brahmananda's Commentary: *When there is no ideation, it is called samadhi. Samprajnata samadhi is described as the absence of ideation.*

काष्ठे प्रवर्त्तितो वह्नि: काष्ठेन सह शाम्यति ।
नादे प्रवर्त्तितं चित्तं नादेन सह लीयते ॥ ९८ ॥

(98) *The fire that burns a piece of wood, dies as soon as the wood is burnt up. So the mind concentrated upon nada gets absorbed with it.*

Brahmananda's Commentary: *Rajasic and tamasic qualities being destroyed, the sattvic quality alone remains. The Maitrayani Mantra says, "Just as the fire, when the fuel is burnt out, is absorbed into its source; so also the mind, when the modifications are destroyed, is absorbed into its source."*

घण्टादिनादसक्तस्तब्धान्त:करणहरिणस्य ।
प्रहरणमपि सुकरं शरसन्धानप्रवीणश्चेत् ॥ ९९ ॥

(99) *When the Antahkarana, like a deer, is attracted to the sounds of bells, etc., and remains immoveable, a skilful archer can kill it.*

Brahmananda's Commentary: *The mind absorbed in the nada, forgets all its modifications. Then the yogi, like an archer, might kill it by directing his breath to the Brahmarandhra through the Sushumna, as said in the **Mundaka Upanishad**. Pranava is the bow, Atman the arrow, and Brahman the mark. If one carefully shoots at the mark, he becomes one with it.*

अनाहतस्य शब्दस्य ध्वनिर्य उपलभ्यते ।
ध्वनेरन्तर्गतं ज्ञेयं ज्ञेयस्यान्तर्गतं मन: ।
मनस्तत्र लयं याति तद्विष्णो: परमं पदम् ॥ १०० ॥

(100) *The self-effulgent Chaitanya (the Absolute Consciousness) exists within the sound proceeding from the Anahata chakra, and the antahkarana (the seat of the Anahata chakra) becomes one with the*

Chaitanya. When the mind is absorbed in it by the
paravairagya, it loses all its modifications and
becomes an abstract thought. This is the supreme
state of the all-pervading Atman who is free from all
the upadhis realized by the yogis.

तावदाकाशसङ्कल्पो यावच्छब्द: प्रवर्तते।
नि:शब्दं तत्परं ब्रह्म परमात्मेति गीयते॥ १०१॥

(101) The conception of akasha (the generator of
sound) exists as long as the sound is heard. The
soundless is called Parabrahman or Paramatman.

Brahmananda's Commentary: *The state in which the mind,
being free from all modifications, exists in the swaroopa, is
called the Parabrahman and the Paramatman.*

यत् किञ्चिन्नादरूपेण श्रूयते शक्तिरेव सा।
यस्तत्त्वान्तो निराकार: स एव परमेश्वर:॥ १०२॥

(102) Whatever is heard in the nature of the
mystical nada is only Shakti. The laya state of the
tattvas is that in which no form exists. That is
Parameshwara, the Supreme Lord.

Brahmananda's Commentary: *From stanzas 98 to this, the
Asamprajnyata samadhi is described. The tattvas are categories
of manifestation according to Sankhya.*

सर्वे हठलयोपाया राजयोगस्य सिद्धये।
राजयोगसमारूढः पुरुषः कालवञ्चकः॥ १०३॥

*(103) All the Hatha and Laya Yoga practices are only
for the attainment of Raja Yoga. Those perfected in
Raja Yoga deceive death.*

तत्त्वं बीजं हठः क्षेत्रमौदासीन्यं जलं त्रिभिः।
उन्मनी कल्पलतिका सद्य एव प्रवर्तते॥ १०४॥

*(104) Mind is the seed, Hatha Yoga is the soil, and
extreme vairagya is the water. By these three, the
Kalpa Vriksha (the tree that gives whatever is
desired), the Unmani (Turiya avastha) springs
up suddenly.*

Brahmananda's Commentary: *The Kalpa Vriksha is a
mythical tree which fulfils all desires. In the Unmani avastha,
which is the transcendental state, all fulfilment is found.*

सदा नादानुसन्धानात् क्षीयन्ते पापसञ्चयाः।
निरञ्जने विलीयेते निश्चितं चित्तमारुतौ॥ १०५॥

*(105) By a constant practice of concentration on
nada, all sins are destroyed. The mind and the prana
certainly become absorbed in the niranjana (the
chaitanya that is devoid of all gunas or attributes).*

शंखदुन्दुभिनादं च न शृणोति कदाचन।
काष्ठवज्जायते देह उन्मन्यावस्थया ध्रुवम्॥ १०६॥

(106) During Unmani Avastha, the body becomes like a log of wood. The yogi never hears the (loud) sounds of a conch or dundubhi (a large drum).

सर्वावस्थाविनिर्मुक्त: सर्वचिन्ताविवर्जित:।
मृतवत्तिष्ठते योगी स मुक्तो नात्र संशय:॥ १०७॥

(107) The yogi who has passed beyond all states and is not troubled by any thoughts (or memories), remains like one dead (impervious to external stimuli). Undoubtedly he is a mukta, emancipated while living.

Brahmananda's Commentary: *There are five states (avasthas): jagrat (waking), swapna (dream), sushupti (deep sleep), moorcha (trance), and marana (death); and these admit of recurrence. The yogi is free from all of these.*

खाद्यते न च कालेन बाध्यते न च कर्मणा।
साध्यते न स केनापि योगी युक्त: समाधिना॥ १०८॥

(108) A yogi in samadhi is not swallowed up by the process of Time (death). He is not influenced by good or bad karma, nor is he affected by anything done against him (by means of invocations, incantations, etc.) to destroy him.

न गन्धं न रसं रूपं न च स्पर्शं न निः स्वनम् ।
नात्मानं न परं वेत्ति योगी युक्तः समाधिना ॥ १०९ ॥

(109) *A yogi in samadhi feels neither smell, taste, touch, sound, shape, nor color. He does not know himself and others.*

चित्तं न सुप्तं नो जाग्रत्स्मृतिविस्मृतिवर्जितम् ।
न चास्तमेति नोदेति यस्यासौ मुक्त एव सः ॥ ११० ॥

(110) *A yogi is called a Jivanmukta when his chitta is neither asleep nor awake, or when he is free from smriti (memory) or vismriti (forgetfulness), or when he is neither dead nor living (in his consciousness).*

Brahmananda's Commentary: *The Antahkarana is said to sleep when tamas (covering all the organs) overcomes both the rajas and the sattva qualities, and when it loses its faculty of discerning objects. It is not awake because it is not in the state of samadhi to experience objects. It is free from smriti (memory) because there are no modifications of the mind, and again, there is no awakening from that state. It is free from vismriti because there are no thoughts conceived by the smriti. It is not destroyed because chitta exists as an abstract thought only. It is not revived because there are no modifications of the mind to set it in action.*

न विजानाति शीतोष्णं न दुःखं न सुखं तथा ।
न मानं नापमानं च योगी युक्तः समाधिना ॥ १११ ॥

(111) A yogi in samadhi does not feel heat or cold, pain or pleasure, honor or disgrace.

स्वस्थो   जाग्रदवस्थायां   सुषुवद्योऽवतिष्ठते।
निःश्वासोच्छ्वासहीनश्च निश्चितं मुक्त एव सः॥ ११२॥

(112) Verily he is a mukta, who, with all his indriyas and mind clear and unclouded, remains in the waking state, yet appears like one in sleep, without inhalation and expiration (due to kumbhaka).

Brahmananda's Commentary: *The mention of the waking state only implies the exclusion of the dream and deep sleep. The yogi appears to be asleep as he is completely motionless.*

अवध्यः सर्वशास्त्राणामशक्यः सर्वदेहिनाम्।
अग्राह्यो मन्त्रयन्त्राणां योगी युक्तः समाधिना॥ ११३॥

(113) A yogi in samadhi is invulnerable to all weapons; all the world cannot overpower him. He is beyond the powers of mantras and tantras (incantations and magical diagrams).

Brahmananda's Commentary: *Some of the things that attract and destroy a yogi in his course are here described: sloth, indifference, loose company, the [negative] practice of mantras, alchemy, and many others. Those who practice Yoga have to encounter these dangers. Fixing the mind on Vishnu or Siva, a yogi surmounts all these difficulties.*

यावन्नैव प्रविशति चरन्मारुतो मध्यमार्गे,
यावद्बिन्दुर्न भवति दृढ:प्राणवातप्रबन्धात्।
यावद्ध्याने सहजसदृशं जायते नैव तत्त्वं,
तावज्ज्ञानं वदति तदिदं दम्भमिथ्याप्रलाप: ॥ ११४ ॥

(114) As long as the prana does not enter the Sushumna and pierce the Brahmarandhra, as long as the bindu (semen) does not become firm from the restraint of breath, as long as the mind (chitta) does not become of the same nature with the object contemplated upon (Brahman) during the dhyana (meditation) – so long are those who talk of dhyana nothing but vain talkers and untruthful men.

Brahmananda's Commentary: *(a) The **Amrita Siddhi** says, "Know him to be a failure in Yoga whose prana has not entered the Sushumna and become absorbed in the Brahmarandhra." (b) Consider him not to be a brahmachari, but an utter failure in Yoga, and subject to old age, death and all sorts of infirmities, as long as he has not controlled his seminal essence and attained the state of samadhi. Such a man is said to be worldly. He is called asiddha (imperfect) though he be practicing Yoga. (c) The **Yoga Bija** says, "When the chitta appears dead, then certainly, prana also appears dead. If the yogi does not experience this, he knows no shastras, no guru, no moksha, and no union with the Atman."*

Krishna says in the **Bhagavatam**, "There are only three ways to liberation laid down by me. They are: jnana, karma, and bhakti." Then why is [Raja] Yoga said to be the chief means of attaining liberation? The answer is that all three are combined in the eight-fold Yoga.

The sruti says, "The Self alone is to be seen, heard, contemplated upon and realized." That Self can be attained by sravana (listening), manana (reflection), and nididhyasana (realization). The first two are included in swadhyaya, which is one of the subdivisions of niyama, the second stage of Yoga. Swadhyaya is the thorough study of the teachings on liberation, with a complete knowledge of their inner meanings and symbolism. Nididhyasana is the restraining of the idea that there is anything else besides Brahman, and the fostering of the realization that everything is Brahman. This is contained in dhyana, the seventh stage of [Raja] Yoga.

Karma Yoga, which is performing all acts as an offering to Ishwara, is contained in the Kriya Yoga described by Patanjali. Patanjali says, "Kriya Yoga is tapas, swadhyaya, and Ishwara pranidhana." Tapas means the purification of the body by the observance of various penances. Swadhyaya consists of those studies that bring about a predominance of the sattva guna. Ishwara pranidhana is praising Ishwara, remembering and worshipping him by word, thought and action, and an unswerving devotion to him.

Bhakti really means the constant perception of the form of the Lord by the inner organ. There are nine kinds of bhakti: hearing the lore concerning the Lord, singing it, remembering Him, worshipping His feet, offering flowers to Him, bowing to Him (in spirit), regarding oneself as His servant, becoming His companion and wholly offering oneself to Him. These are all included in Ishwara pranidhana. Bhakti has been described by Narayana Tirtha as an unbroken stream of love towards the feet of the Lord – a love that is the be all and end all of a person's existence, and during which he is, as it were, absorbed in the object of his devotion. Madhusudana Saraswati has also described it as a state of mind, when previous to its being utterly annihilated and absorbed, it becomes of the nature of the Lord. Thus Bhakti, in its most transcendental aspect, is included in Samprajnata samadhi.

So the three ways laid down by Krishna in the **Bhagavatam** have been shown to be included in the stages of Yoga. Thus Yoga practiced in its entirety, and in the order laid down, is enough for the attainment of liberation. In this sense alone are to be understood the words in the Puranas saying that Brahman is to be attained by Yoga.

EPILOGUE

Address delivered by Swami Vishnu-devananda at the Final Ceremony of the Yoga Sadhana Intensive at the Sivananda Ashram Yoga Camp during June, 1987.

As many of you know, the *Hatha Yoga Pradipika* is the original treatise on Hatha Yoga. It was written down by Swami Swatmarama, whose name means "he who is sporting with his own Atman." We on the other hand, are "Bhogaramas," because we sport with our own senses.

Modern Hatha Yoga has been developed and enlarged from Swatmarama's book. There are three other classical treatises on Hatha Yoga: the *Siva Samhita, Gherandha Samhita,* and the *Goraksha Samhita.* They are all within the tradition of Ashtanga Yoga (the eight-limbed Yoga). Raja Yoga, Hatha Yoga, Kundalini Yoga, Laya Yoga, Mantra Yoga are all part of Ashtanga Yoga. They differ a little bit only in approach.

Of the eight steps of Ashtanga Yoga, yama and niyama are common to all these Yogas. Asanas (or postures) were not elaborated on too much by some of these treatises; Patanjali's *Yoga Sutras* is an example. He describes only one asana, saying only that sitting comfortably in a pose is asana. He did not elaborate beyond that because in those days people were practicing cultural poses in their daily lives as part of the Gurukhula system of education.

Under the Gurukhula system, a student goes to live under the guidance of the teacher for ten to twelve years. The teacher might have thirty or forty students. He would have a little plot of land and simple accommodations, a few cows or other cattle for their livelihood. The students would help in tilling the land, cultivating, and milking the cows. In return, the teacher would impart his knowledge. Part of the knowledge imparted was that of asanas and pranayama; they were given to all, beginners as well as advanced students. Every child had to perform pranayama with the Gayatri mantra.

Yama and niyama (ethics and morals), were all practiced in daily life. Hatha yogis elaborated on the regulations concerning cleanliness, not only by cleaning the teeth and the rest of the body, but going even deeper - cleaning the nasal passages, the stomach, etc. And even further, into advanced cleaning through pranayama and through the Bija mantras of the elements. For example, the Bija mantra of earth is Lam, Vam is the Bija mantra for water, Ram is the Bija mantra for fire, Tam is the Bija mantra for the moon. Gross matter of any kind is called earth, any liquid is water, any fire is called Ram, and any energy which cools the body and brings purification is called Tam, or moon, or nectar. So, by using various Bija mantras, you are purifying the system through subtle pranayama. In the Gurukhula system there was the practice of such things as Bija mantras, so there was no need for Patanjali or other Raja yogis to describe them. Students learned these practices directly from the teacher.

Although asanas were not elaborated on by Patanjali and other Raja yogis, they were performed to cause the body to become very still. The cultural poses trained the body so that it could be kept still and steady without strain or effort. When such a pose is found - one that is easy and comfortable for you - stick to it all of your life. You will get rock-like firmness, and your nerve energy will start flowing when you use it for meditation. Your metabolic activity, breathing mechanism, pulse rate, and blood pressure will go down. As these metabolic activities slow down when you sit quietly, you attain the first step of Raja Yoga.

Then you go to the second level, pranayama. Again, Patanjali only says this much: that regulation of inhalation and exhalation is pranayama. Its purpose is to reduce the velocity of the mind. People were practicing other pranayamas: Anuloma Viloma, Bhastrika, Ujjayi, Surya bedha - so they understood that prana is not the physical air. They learned these techniques also from the guru, as it was part of their daily routine. That is why Raja Yoga had no need to go into detail; Patanjali didn't have to elaborate on it as it was common knowledge. Only later on, when people's minds began wandering because they no longer had the discipline, and the Gurukhula system declined, then at that time Swatmarama introduced Hatha Yoga. It is for the same end as Raja Yoga, but it now has to explain those asanas and pranayamas which had been taught as part of the Gurukhula system.

The fourth step is pratyahara or withdrawal of the mind from the senses, or introversion. Patanjali says, *"Yoga chitta vritti nirodha."* Yoga is stilling the mental modifications of the mind. Raja Yoga elaborated these three processes, and so did Swatmarama Yogi, but in a way that gave more control. Most people, by merely closing their eyes, cannot regulate their thoughts. But when they perform pranayama, mudras or bandhas properly, then the prana moves in the Sushumna, causing the mind to become very still. Raja Yoga does not say how to achieve this mental state except through stopping the mind. The teacher would also have taught the student how to perform bandhas and mudras in the Gurukhula system, so Patanjali only gives the theory of concentration and samyama.

Samyama is concentration, meditation, and samadhi; they are only varying amounts of mental control. Concentration's quality is less, in meditation quality is a little better. In meditation, your mind is pure like a candle which is steady when there is no wind. Patanjali says that you can do samyama on anything, using these three processes, and get the knowledge of that particular element. Suppose you are concentrating on Lam (in the Muladhara chakra, representing the earth element), then earth won't affect you; you will have power over earth, solid matter. Raja Yoga explains the theory, but Hatha Yoga puts it into practice. And that is the intense sadhana described in these pages.

They are almost the same activities I performed when I was in the Himalayas undergoing my own training. With Gurudev's Grace and with His blessings, I went to Uttarkashi and I followed this same program. Morning, midday, evening, and midnight I practiced pranayama, asanas, bandhas, plus about 200 malas of mantra (taking about three or four hours). I had hardly two or three hours of sleep each night, but that was sufficient for the body. It doesn't need too much because intense energy starts flowing. You can experience these things.

With God's Grace and with Guru's Grace we have been able to do intense sadhana to purify the physical body, the astral body, and the causal body. As I mentioned before, all asanas, pranayama, bandhas and mudras end in Kevala kumbhaka, in Unmani avastha (the natural state). The natural state is that state where there is no duality. Kevala kumbhaka means suspension of prana in the Ida and Pingala so that the prana moves only in the Sushumna.

It took innumerable births for you to reach this stage. Do not stop your practices now. Lead a moderate and dedicated life. Do not go too fast and then stop the practices because of kickback. Do not go so slow that you get discouraged from lack of visible progress.

Do not be anxious, constantly thinking of your spiritual progress. There will be ups and downs. It is not a straight path. Be courageous. Climb. There will be so many falls; so many ascents you will have to make; so many ropes to tie. There will be so many camps you have to make: base camp, second camp, third camp, fourth camp, and finally, no camp at all when you are left alone to reach the final summit. Nobody to help you now, you will be there alone. But you are not disheartened as you want to reach the top.

In this very life, seek the summit. Pray. Surrender. Our will needs God's Grace, because our will is only a drop. God's Grace is like the ocean. Our willpower is not sufficient to cross the ocean of samsara. Our effort is like a tiny boat with broken oars crossing the Atlantic Ocean; only God's Grace will see us across the ocean.

You must have dispassion and discrimination. While immersed in the activities of life, it is very difficult to keep dispassion, it is very difficult to keep discrimination. But don't forget your goal. Keep Mount Everest always in view. Always look up. Go up a little bit more each time, till your last breath. Never stop your sadhana, your evolution. Look always up, up, up. Go onwards always. It doesn't matter in which state you are, still you have to climb. Never be satisfied with your progress, with your success, with your mental control, because that same mind is waiting for you.

There will be rocks, snow, glaciers, so you will have to go to the right and to the left, but still you will trip and fall. Always pray to God, "Help me, let me not fall again." Prostrate. Surrender to Him. Your effort alone is not sufficient. You can't see the hidden pitfalls. But with surrender, and with your straightforward and honest practice of yama and niyama, you will reach the goal.

May the Lord Bless you with success and liberation in this very lifetime.

Swami Vishnu-devananda

Swami Vishnu-devananda

GLOSSARY
OF SANSKRIT TERMS
[Guide to pronounciation is within brackets]

Abhinivesa: Earnest desire; ardent longing; perserverence; clinging to life.

Achamana: [Aachamana] Sipping of water to purify before religious ceremonies.

Acharya: [Aacharya] Spiritual guide or perceptor.

Adhibhoutika: [Aadhibhoutika] Suffering caused by animals; bee stings, snake bites, attacks by lions, amoebic dysentery, etc.

Adhidaivika: [Aadhidaivika] Suffering caused by planetary influences; natural disasters such as earthquakes, floods, windstorms, etc.

Adhyatmika: [Aadhyatmika] Physical (bodily) and mental suffering.

Adikari: a sincere spiritual aspirant with proper qualifications.

Adinatha: [Aadinaatha] The first Lord; a name for Siva.

Advaita: Non-dualistic philosophy.

Aham: 'I' or ego.

Ahimsa: [Ahimsaa] Non-violence in thought, word and deed; mercy. This is one of the Yamas (restrictions) of Raja Yoga.

Ajna: [Aajna] The sixth chakra; the centre of spiritual energy between the two eyebrows; the "third eye."

Akasha: [Aakasha] Space; ether.

Anahata: [Anaahata] (1) The fourth chakra, corresponding to the heart plexus. (2) Astral, "unstruck" or soundless sounds. Mystical sound which is heard by yogis.

Ananda: [Aananda] Bliss, joy, infinite happiness.

Ananta: (1) The thousand-headed serpent on which Vishnu reclines. (2) Endless.

Anima: One of the eight major siddhis; the power to assume a minute form.

Antahkarana: The inner instrument. The ego or "self arrogating" principle.

Anuloma Viloma: Alternate nostril breathing.

Apana: [Apaana] The downward-moving manifestation of Prana, controls excretion and all the functions of the lumbar region of the autonomic nervous system. The seat of apana is in the anus; its color is a mixture of red and white.

Aparigraha: Non-receiving of presents (bribes). One of the Yama (restrictions) of Raja Yoga.

Asamprajnata samadhi: [Asamprajnaata samaadhi] Superconscious state where the mind is totally annihilated, and Reality is experienced. Having no consciousness of the triad; knower, knowledge and the known become one. The highest state of Raja Yoga.

Asamsakti: A person who is unaffected by anything. The yogi is now known as Brahmavidvara. This is the fifth stage of Jnana (Knowledge).

Asana: [Aasana] Posture or position. Poses for meditation and/or body control.

Ashtanga: [Astaanga] Eight limbed; Ashtanga Yoga is another name for Raja Yoga.

Ashram: [Aashram] Hermitage or monastery.

Ashwini mudra: A practice to help to control the sex urge; while sitting in water, contract and release the anal sphincter muscles, trying to draw the prana upwards.

Asmita: Egoism.

Asteya: Non-covetousness; lack of jealousy. This is one of the Yamas (restrictions) of Raja Yoga.

Astikya: [Aastikya] Belief in God.

Asura: A demon; a being of darkness.

Atman: [Aatman] The individual soul; the Self.

Avatara: [Avataara] An incarnation of God in physical form.

Avidya: [Avidyaa] Ignorance.

Bandha: Muscular locks applied by yogis during certain breathing exercises. These are essential in advanced pranayama, in order to direct and unite the prana and apana. For further details, see pages 247-250 in *Complete Illustrated Book of Yoga*.

Basti: Lower colon irrigation/cleansing; one of the Shad kriyas.

Bhadrasana: [Bhadraasana] Described in *Hatha Yoga Pradipika*, chapter 1, vs 53,54; in *Complete Illustrated Book of Yoga*, see plates 116-117; also known as Gorakshana.

Bhagavad Gita: [Bhagavad Geeta] Literally translated as the "Song of God," this is one of the great Hindu scriptures.

Bhagavatam: [Bhaagavatam] The Purana (a category of Hindu scriptures) dealing with the exploits and incarnations of Vishnu.

Bhakta: A spiritual devotee. A follower of the path of Bhakti Yoga.

Bhakti Yoga: The path of devotion.

Bharata-varsa: [Bhaarata-varsa] India

Bhastrika: An important, slightly advanced pranayama. Forcefully inhaling and exhaling like the bellows of a blacksmith. It has the effect of neither heating nor cooling, but of bringing the body into balance. See chapter 2, vs 59-67.

Bhava samadhi: [Bhaava samadhi] The highest state of Bhakti Yoga in which the devotee has the attitude of identification with the Divine.

Bhogaramas: [Bhogaaraamaas] Those people who indulge in pleasure and live for enjoyment.

Bija mantra: The seed or root syllable which contains a specific power.

Bindu: The dot, or point, which is the center of the nucleus. Static energy.

Brahma: [Brahmaa] The Creator, in the Hindu trinity of Brahma, Vishnu and Siva; not be be confused with Brahman (the Absolute).

Brahmachari: [Brahmachaari] A student; one who practices brahmacharya.

Brahmacharya: Celibacy, or control of the sexual energy. This is one of the Yamas (restrictions) of Raja Yoga.

Brahma granthi: First knot in the Sushumna, located at the Muladhara chakra.

Brahman: The Absolute Reality.

Brahma nadi: [Brahma naadi]Another name for Sushumna.

Brahmarandhra: Literal meaning is "Brahma's Canal" or "the entry to Brahman," it is located in the center of the Sushumna nadi. Opening of the skull; head fontanelle.

Brahmari: A minor pranayama; a light variety of breathing exercise. See chapter 2, vs 68.

Brahmavaristha: A yogi who has attained the seventh, and highest, stage of Jnana, who remains in a state of perpetual samadhi.

Brahmavid: Knower of Brahman; a sadhak who has reached the Sattvapatti (fourth) stage of Jnana.

Brahmavidvara: A yogi who has reached the Asamsakti (fifth) stage of Jnana.

Brahmavidya: The science of Brahman.

Buddhi: Intellect.

Chaitanya: Pure consciousness.

Chakra: The astral centers, located in the Sushumna.

Chit: Consciousness.

Chitta: The subconscious mind.

Crore: Ten million; one hundred lakhs.

Dana: [Daana] Giving of charity.

Deva: A god or angel; a celestial being.

Dharana: [Dhaarana] Concentration; the sixth limb of Raja Yoga.

Dharma: Righteous conduct.

Dhatus: The tissues of the body: skin, flesh, blood, bones, marrow, fat, and semen.

Dhauti: Cleansing of the upper digestive tract (i.e. mouth, oesophagus and stomach); one of the Shad kriyas.

Dhanurasana: [Dhanuraasana] The "Bow" Pose. *Hatha Yoga Pradipika*, chapter 1, vs 25. In the *Complete Illustrated Book of Yoga*, this is referred to as Akarna Dhanurasan (Shooting Bow Pose), plate 125-127.

Dhyana: [Dhyaana] Meditation; the seventh limb of Raja Yoga.

Drusthi: Seeing, viewing. Seeing with the mental eye.

Dvesha: Repulsion; hatred.

Gajakarani: Also known as Kunja kriya or Gaja karma. In this form of Dhauti, a large quantity of lukewarm water is drunk and then vomited up.

Gandhara: One of the ten major nadis.

Gariman: One of the eight major siddhis; the power to become very heavy.

Gayatri: [Gaayatri] One of the most sacred Vedic mantras; goddess.

Gita: [Geeta] Usually referring to Bhagavad Gita.

Gomukhasana: [Go'mukhaasana] "Cow's Head Pose," described in *Hatha Yoga Pradipika*, chapter 1, vs 20; in *Complete Illustrated Book of Yoga*, see plate 122.

Gorakshasana: [Gorakshaasana] Another name for Bhadrasana.

Granthi: Three (Brahma, Vishnu and Rudra) knots, or protective blockages in the Sushumna. Their purpose is to block the upward flow of prana. They function as fuses or circuit breakers to protect the practitioner from an energy overload. The knots will only open when sufficient purification and strengthening has taken place.

Grihastha: A householder, or married person.

Guna: Quality or attribute. One of three qualities of Nature (or Prakriti): Sattva, Rajas and Tamas.

Guptasana: [Guptaasana] See chapter 1, vs 37; also known as Muktasan

Guru: Teacher or perceptor.

Gurukhula: The system by which the student went to live in the teacher's ashram. The perceptor's hermitage.

Guruparampara: The guru-disciple lineage.

Hatha Yoga: The path of Yoga giving first attention to the physical body, which is a vehicle for the spirit; preference is given to the mobilization of the body and the control of the vital breath.
It can be divided as follows:
1. Internal and external purification of the physical body (Kriyas).
2. Practice of Asanas (physical exercises).
3. Practice of Mudras and Bandhas
4. Pranayama: control of the vital energy.
5. Pratyahara: withdrawing the mental energy from external stimulation.
6. Dharana: Concentration.
7. Dhyana: Meditation.
8: Samadhi: Superconscious state, when the individual consciousness, or ego, merges with the Supreme Consciousness, or Brahman.

Hiranyagarbha: Literally meaning "born of a golden egg." Cosmic mind.

Ida: The nadi to the left of the Sushumna. Its nature is intuitive, holistic, inner-directed, emotional, subjective, feminine, cool.

Indriya: Sense organ. There are 5 Jnana indriyas (organs of knowledge: taste, touch, smell, sight and hearing) and 5 Karma indriyas (organs of action: hands, feet, tongue, anus and genitals).

Ishwara: God in the form of the chosen deity. Brahman as filtered through the Upadis.

Ishwarapranidana: [Ishwarapranidaana] Surrender to the will of God or surrender of the ego. One of the Niyamas (prescribed observances) of Raja Yoga.

Isita: One of the eight major siddhis; the power to shape anything as desired.

Jagrat: The awake state of consciousness.

Jalandhara bandha: [Jaalandhara bandha] The chin lock, forcing the prana downward. The chin is brought down to touch the Kantha kupa (sternal notch).

Jala neti: One of the Shad kriyas; water is poured into one nostril and comes out by the other (or through the mouth).

Jambu-dvipa: [Jambu-dveepa] Indian sub-continent.

Janaka: Name of a royal sage.

Japa: Repetition of Mantras or God's name.

Jihva bandha: [Jihvaa bandha] The tongue lock, to be done with Jalandhara bandha. The top of the tongue is flat against the roof of the mouth and drawn back as much as possible.

Jiva(tman): [Jeevaa] The individual soul.

Jivanmukti: [Jeevanmukti] Self-realization while living.

Jnana: [Jnaana] Knowledge; wisdom.

Jnana Yoga: [Jnaana Yoga] The intellectual or philosophical path.

Jnani: [Jnaani] A sage or wise person.

Jyoti: Light.

Kaivalya: Absoluteness. Isolated freedom; state of absolute independence.

Kala: The transcendental wave; the energy which makes the electrons whirl around the nucleus. A ray, digit of manifestation.

Kali-yuga: The last of the four Hindu time cycles; the present "Iron Age."

Kanda: The place near the navel where the nadis unite and separate. It is described as soft, white and egg-like, covered by membraneous membranes. From the kanda spring the 72,000 nadis. It is like a battery, with wires (nadis) going to all parts of the (astral) body. Some yogis equate the kanda with the perineum, the space between the two legs.

Kapalabhati: [Kapaalabhati] Literally translated as "shining skull." Breathing exercise for cleansing the respiratory system. One of the Shad kriyas (six cleansing exercises).

Karma: Action; the law of action and reaction, or cause and effect.

Kevala kumbhaka: Absolute or natural retention (with no effort).

Khechari mudra: See chapter 3, vs 33-43.

Kirtan(a): Singing the Lord's Name.

Kleshas: [Kleshaas] Pain, anguish, suffering, distress, trouble.

Kriya: A cleansing or purificatory exercise.

Kukkutasana: [Kukkutaasana] The "Cock" pose, described in *Hatha Yoga Pradipika*, chapter 1, vs 23; in *Complete Illustrated Book of Yoga*, see plate 114.

Kumbhaka: Retention of breath.

Kundalini: Serpent Power; the primordial cosmic energy located in the individual.

Kunja(l) kriya: In this form of Dhauti, a large quantity of lukewarm water is drunk and then vomited up.

Laghiman: One of the eight major siddhis; the power to become very light.

Lakh: One hundred thousand (100,000).

Laya: Absorption of mind. Merging; dissolution.

Linga(m): Symbol of Siva, representing the unmanifested. An imageless image.

Lotus Pose: Padmasana; see chapter 1, vs 21, 23, 34, 44-49.

Madhyamarga: Literally translated as "the middle path," it is usually used to refer to the Sushumna.

Maha bandha: [Mahaabandha] See chapter 3, vs 19-24.

Maha mudra: [Mahaamudra] See chapter 3, vs 14-18.

Mahapatha: [Mahaapatha] "the great road"; refers to the Sushumna.

Mahatma: [Mahaatmaa] A great soul; a saint.

Maha vedha: [Mahaavedha] See chaper 3, vs 25-29.

Maheswara: [Maheshwara] The Great Lord; a name for Siva.

Mahiman: One of the eight major siddhis; the power to assume a large form.

Mala: (1) An impurity of the mind: lust, anger, greed etc. (2) A garland or necklace.

Manomani Avasta: The state attained when the prana enters the Sushumna.

Manana: Thinking, reflection, cogitation; an inference arrived at by reasoning. This is an aspect of Swadyaya (study).

Manas: Mind.

Manipura Chakra: The third chakra, located in the nabhi (navel) in the Sushumna.

Marana: (1) Death, one of the 5 avasthas (states of consciousness). (2) Killing, destruction. (3) A magical ceremony performed for the purpose of destroying an enemy.

Matha or math: A cottage; a small ashram or monastery

Matra: [Maatra] An ancient measure of time; approximately 3 seconds.

Matsyendrasana: [Matsyendraasana] Spinal Twist. Described in *Hatha Yoga Pradipika* chapter 1, vs 27; In *Complete Illustrated Book of Yoga*, see plate 101-104.

Mayurasana: [Mayuraasana] The "Peacock" pose. Described in *Hatha Yoga Pradipika* chapter 1, vs 30; in *Complete Illustrated Book of Yoga*, plates 105-109.

Meru: The fabulous mountain at the centre of the universe, around which all the planets are said to revolve. The central bead in a mala, or rosary.

Moksha: Liberation.

Moorcha or Murcha: (1) A minor pranayama; a light variety of yogic breathing. (2) Trance state, one of the 5 avasthas (states of consciousness). See chapter 2, vs 99

Mudra: (1) Hatha Yoga exercises, usually used with bandhas, whose purpose is to seal the union of prana-apana. (2) In Indian dance: hand gestures.

Muktasana: [Muktaasana] Also known as Guptasana; see chapter 1, vs 37.

Mukti: Emancipation.

Mula (or Moola) bandha: The anal lock, forcing the apana upward.

Muladhara chakra: [Mooladhaara chakra] The first, or lowest, center of spiritual energy located at the base of the spine.

Mumukshutva: A burning desire for liberation and an intense striving to attain it. One of the four necessary qualifications of a serious student of yoga.

Muni: An ascetic.

Nada: [Naada] Mystical sound. Sound or energy wave. Nada and bindu are represented by Siva and Shakti. Nada is the electrons whirling around the nucleus.

Nadi: [Naadi] An astral nerve. The Sanskrit term equivalent to the "meridians" of acupuncture.

Narakas: [Narakaas] Hells; places of purification after death.

Narayana: [Naraayana] Vishnu, the preserver of the Hindu trinity.

Nataraja: [Nataraaja] The dancing Lord Siva.

Nauli: Manipulation and churning of the abdomen; one of the Shad kriyas (six cleansing exercises).

Neelakantha: or Nilakantha. "Blue-throated"; a name for Siva.

Neti: Cleansing of the upper respiratory tract (i.e. nose, nasal passages, sinuses); one of the Shad Kriyas (six cleansing exercises).

Nididhyasana: [Nididhyaasana] Realization of the Truth. Profound and deep meditation.

Niralamba: [Niraalamba] Without support.

Niranjana: The pure consciousness which is free of all qualities or attributes.

Nirvikalpa samadhi: [Nirvikalpa samaadhi] The superconscious state where the mental modifications cease to exist. The term used in Jnana Yoga.

Niyama: Religious observances, such as cleanliness, contentment, austerity, study and worship of God; the second limb of Raja Yoga.

Om: The sacred monosyllable which symbolizes the Absolute.

Om Namah Sivaya: [Om Namah Shivaaya] The Panchakshara (five-lettered) mantra of Lord Siva.

Om Namo Narayanaya: [Om Namo Naaraayanaaya] The mantra of Vishnu.

Padma: Lotus.

Padmasana: [Padmaasana] (see Lotus Pose).

Papa: [Paapa] Sin.

Parabrahman: The Absolute.

Paramatman: [Paramaatman] The Supreme Self.

Pararthabhavani: [Paraarthabhaavani] The sixth stage of Jnana, where external things do not appear to exist.

Parashakti: [Paraashakti] The highest energy; Kundalini. The Supreme Goddess.

Parvati: [Paarvati] Lord Siva's consort.

Paschimottanasana: [Paschimottanaasana] The Forward Bend pose, Described in *Hatha Yoga Pradipika* chapter 2, vs 28-29. In *Complete Illustated Book of Yoga,* see plates 55-57.

Patanjali: [Paatanjali] Author of the Raja Yoga Sutras.

Pingala: The nadi to the right side of the Sushumna; its nature is aggressive, logical, sequential, analytical, outer-directed, rational, objective, hot, masculine, directing mathematical and verbal activities.

Plavini: [Plaavini] A minor pranayama; a light variety of yogic breathing exercise. See chapter 2, vs 70.

Prakamya: [Prakaamya] One of the eight major siddhis; the power to obtain whatever is desired.

Prana: [Praana] The vital force. Although prana is one, it takes five major forms (i.e. prana, apana, samana, udana and vyana). Prana governs the cervical portion of the autonomic nervous system, the verbal mechanism and the vocal apparatus, the respiratory system and the movements of the gullet. The seat of prana is in the heart; its color is that of a red gem.

Pranava: The sacred monosyllable OM.

Pranayama: [Praanaayaama} The science of breath control. Control of the Prana (vital energy).

Prapti: [Praapti] One of the eight major siddhis; the power to reach distant objects.

Prarabdha: [Praarabdha] The karma which has been chosen to be worked out in this lifetime.

Pratyahara: [Pratyaahaara] Abstraction of the senses; withdrawal of the mental energy from the senses. The fifth step of Raja Yoga.

Punya: merit.

Puraka: [Pooraka] Inhalation of breath.

Purana: [Poorana] Eighteen scriptures of Hindu myths and legends. Sacred works dealing with the doctrines of creation, etc.

Purusha: The Supreme Being.

Raga: [Raaga] (1) Attachment. (2) A tune.

Raja Yoga: [Raaja Yoga] The kingly science; the eight-limbed Yoga of Maharishi Patanjali.

Rajas: Activity, passion, stimulation, restlessness.

Rajoguna: The quality of Rajas, or activity; one of its symptoms is fickleness of mind.

Ramayana: [Raamaayana] The Hindu epic dealing with the life of Sri Rama.

Rechaka: Exhalation of breath.

Rishi: A seer or sage.

Rudra granthi: The last knot in the Sushumna; it is located at the Ajna chakra.

Sadhaka: [Saadhaka] A spiritual aspirant; a seeker.

Sadhana: [Saadhana] Spiritual practice.

Sahaja: Natural.

Sahasrara: [Sahasraara] The eight or highest chakra; the "thousand petal lotus." The highest psychic centre wherein the yogi attains union between the individual soul and the universal soul.

Sahita kumbhaka: The regular retention of breath, either inside or outside of the body.

Samadhi: [Samaadhi] The Superconscious state.

Samana: [Samaana] One of the five major pranas; performs digestion and controls secretions of the digestive system throughout the sympathetic nervous system in the thoracic region. Its seat is in the region of the navel; its color is between that of pure milk and crystal.

Samhita: Classical texts on Hatha Yoga include: *Siva Samhita, Gherandha Samhita, Goraksha Samhita.*

Samprajnata samadhi: [Samprajnaata samaadhi] Contemplation where the consciousness of duality still lingers.

Samsara: [Samsaara] The continuous round, or wheel, of births and deaths.

Samskaras: [Samskaaraas] Subtle impressions of past lives.

Samyama: The simultaneous occurrence of concentration, meditation, and samadhi in a developed yogi.

Sanchar: [Sanchaar] Awakening of.

Sandhyavandana: [Sandhyaavandana] Prayers at dawn and dusk.

Sankalpa: Thought, imagination.

Sannyasi(n): [Sanyaasi(n)] A renunciate; a monk.

Santosha: Contentment. One of the Niyamas (prescribed observances) of Raja Yoga.

Satchidananda: [Satchidaananda] Existence Absolute, Knowledge Absolute, Bliss Absolute.

Sattva: The quality of purity.

Sattvapatti: [Sattvaapatti] Attainment of the state of purity; fourth state of Jnana (Knowledge).

Satyam: Truthfulness. This is one of the Yamas (restrictions) of Raja Yoga.

Saucha: Cleanliness or purity. One of the Niyamas (prescribed observances) of Raja Yoga.

Savasana: [Shavaasana] The Corpse pose; chapter 1, vs 32. In *Complete Illustrated Book of Yoga*, see plate 146.

Sesha: (1) The thousand-headed serpent on which Vishnu sleeps. (2) Balance, remainder, what is left.

Shad kriyas: The six cleansing exercises, i.e. Neti, Nauli, Dhauti, Basti, Tratak and Kapalabhati.

Shad sampat: The six-fold virtues.

Shakti: Power, energy. Goddess. Female power.

Shakti chalini: [Shakti chaalini] An exercise for raising the Kundalini.

Shambhavi: [Shaambhavi] Pertaining to the auspicious Shambu, the term is often used to refer to the Sushumna.

Shambhu: Happiness; one who grants prosperity. A name for Siva.

Shanmukhi mudra: Also known as Yoni mudra. Each ear is closed with the thumb, each eye with the forefinger, the nose with the middle fingers, and the mouth with ring and little fingers.

Shankaracharya: [Shankaraachaarya] The ninth century philosopher and exponent of Advaita Vedanta. Founder of the Swami orders of monks.

Shastras: [Shaastraas] Scriptures.

Shunya: [Shoonya] The void; without time or space awareness; having no qualities.

Siddha: One who possesses Siddhis or psychic powers.

Siddhasana: [Siddhaasana] Many yogis feel that this is the most important of all the 84 lakh asanas.

Siddhis: Psychic powers.

Simhasana: [Simhaasana] The "Lion" Pose, described in *Hatha Yoga Pradipika* chapter 1, vs 50-52. In *Complete Illustrated Book of Yoga*, see plate 145.

Sitali: [Seetali] A minor pranayama performed with the tongue folded in half; a light breathing exercise which is cooling to the body. See chapter 2, vs 57-58

Sitkari: [Seetkari] A minor pranayama performed with the tongue folded back; a light breathing exercise which is cooling to the body. See chapter 2, vs 54-56.

Siva: [Shiva] The destructive aspect of Godhead, the third of the Hindu Trinity; also, the Supreme Lord. The bestower of auspiciousness on His devotees.

Sloka: A scriptural verse.

Smarana: Remembrance.

Smasana: [Smasaana] Literally translated as "the burning ground," it is another name for the Sushumna.

Smriti: That which has been remembered. Works of law-givers like Manu which are inferior to the Sruti or revealed scriptures on a point of religious authority.

Soma: Nectar of the moon; divine nectar.

Srimad Bhagavatham: [Srimad Bhaagavatham] The holy scripture of the Hindus wherein the life and teachings of Krishna appear; the incarnations of Vishnu and attendant philosophy are explained.

Sravana: Listening to spiritual or religious discourse; an aspect of Swadyaya.

Srutis: Scriptures which are heard.

Subechcha: [Subechchaa] Longing for the Truth; the first stage of Jnana (Knowledge).

Sunyapadavi: [Shoonyapadavi] The great void.

Surya: [Soorya] The Sun.

Surya bheda: [Soorya bheda] An advanced pranayama which increases the heat in the body; see chapter 2, vs 48-50.

Sushumna: The central nadi, or astral nerve, which runs through the spinal cord.

Sushupti: Deep sleep, one of the 5 avasthas (states of consciousness).

Sutra neti: [Sootra neti] One of the Shad kriyas in which a string (or catheter) is passed through the nose and comes out the mouth, with the purpose of cleansing the nasal passage.

Swadhyaya: [Swaadhyaaya] Study of scriptures, or spiritual books. One of the Niyamas (prescribed observances) of Raja Yoga.

Swapna: Dream state of consciousness.

Swaroopa: Essence; the essential nature of Brahman.

Swastikasana: [Swastikaasana] An important sitting pose, described in *Hatha Yoga Pradipika* chapter 1, vs 19. In *Complete Illustrated Book of Yoga,* see plates 17-18.

Swatmarama: [Swaatmaaraama] Author of *Hatha Yoga Pradipika;* the literal translation of his name is "he who is sporting with his own Atman."

Tamas: The quality (guna) of darkness, inertia and infatuation.

Tamasic: [Taamasic] Impure, rotten (with reference to food), lazy, dull.

Tantras: [Tantraas] A path of Sadhana laying great stress upon repetition of Mantra and other esoteric meditations.

Tanumanasa: [Tanumaanasa] Fading out of the mind; the third stage of Jnana (Knowledge).

Tapas: Austerities, or penances. One of the Niyamas (prescribed observances) of Raja Yoga.

Tattva: Principle; the Supreme Principle or Brahman.

Tratak: [Traatak] Steady gazing with the purpose of cleansing and strengthening the eyes and frontal region. It also improves concentration. One of the Shad Kriyas.

Turiya: [Tureeya] (1) The state wherein the yogi sees God everywhere. (2) The state of superconsciousness, the fourth state transcending the waking, dreaming and deep sleep states.

Udana: [Udaana] One of the five major pranas with its seat in the throat, Udana controls the swallowing of food and the duties which take the individual to sleep. Its realm of activity is above the larynx and it controls all the automatic functions of the autonomic nervous system that take place in the skull. Udana also functions as a psychic force that separates the astral body from the physical body at the time of death.

Uddiyana bandha: [Uddiyaana bandha] One of the three most important bandhas, in which the belly is contracted after exhalation.

Ujjayi: An advanced pranayama; see chapter 2, vs 51-53.

Umani Avastha: Hatha Yoga samadhi through control of the prana.

Upadhi: [Upaadhi] Limiting adjunct.

Uttana Kurmasana: [Uttana Kurmaasana] The "Lifted Tortoise" pose, described in chapter 1, vs 24. In *Complete Illustrated Book of Yoga*, see plate 131. Also known as Garbhasana (foetus pose).

Uttarkashi: Himalayan region where Swami Vishnu-devananda did his period of intensive sadhana.

Vairagya: [Vairaagya] Dispassion. Perfect indifference to any object of desire of earthly life.

Vajrasana: [Vajraasana] Kneeling pose; Energy pose.

Vajroli mudra: A practice which is not followed in sattvic sadhana.

Vasanas: [Vaasanaas] Subtle desires.

Vasitva: One of the eight major siddhis; the power to control anything.

Vayu: [Vaayu] Air; gaseous matter.

Vedanta: [Vedaanta] Literal meaning is "the end of the Vedas." The school of thought based primarily on the Upanishads. The philosophy of Oneness; the end (goal) of Knowledge.

Vedas: [Vedaas] The revealed scripture of the Hindus containing the Upanishads.

Veena (sometimes spelt Vina): An ancient stringed musical instrument.

Vicharana: [Vichaarana] Right inquiry; the second stage of Jnana (Knowledge).

Vidya: [Vidyaa] Knowledge, science, art.

Viparita karani: Literal translation is "Topsy turvey" pose; see chapter 3, vs 79-82.

Virasana: [Viraasana] Also known as Padmasana; chapter 1, vs 21.

Vishnu granthi: The second knot in the Sushumna, located at the Manipura chakra.

Vismriti: Forgetfulness.

Visuddha: The fifth chakra, located at the throat.

Viveka: Discrimination between what is permanent and impermanent.

Viveka Chudamani: [Viveka Choodamani] (Crest Jewel of Discrimination) Sankaracharya's masterpiece of Vedantic philosophy.

Vrata: Vow; religious observance.

Vritti: Thought wave; a wave on the mind-lake. Mental modification.

Vyana: [Vyaana] One of the five major pranas, Vyana performs the circulation of blood. It controls the voluntary and involuntary movements of the muscles, joints and surrounding structures. Its color resembles that of a ray of light. Vyana also helps to keep the body in an erect position by generating unconscious reflexes along the spinal cord; it is all-pervading and moves throughout the entire body.

Vyomachakra: Another name for Khechari mudra.

Yama: (1) Ethics, restrictions; the first limb of Raja Yoga. Internal purification through moral training. (2) Death (Time). The Lord of Death. (3) A three-hour period.

Yoga Vasistha: An important scripture on Advaita Vedanta philosophy, written in the form of conversation between Rama and his guru, the sage Vasistha.

INDEX

SUGGESTED FURTHER READING

COMPLETE ILLUSTRATED BOOK OF YOGA by Swami Vishnu-devananda, published by Crown Publishers, New York.

GHERANDA SAMHITA translated by Rai Bahadur Srisa Chandra Vasu, published by Oriental Books Reprint Corporation, New Delhi.

HATHA YOGA PRADIPIKA translated by Pancham Sinh, published by Munshiram Manoharlal Publishers, New Delhi.

KUNDALINI YOGA by Swami Sivananda, published by the Divine Life Society, Rishikesh, India.

MEDITATION AND MANTRAS by Swami Vishnu-devananda, published by OM Lotus Publishing Company, New York.

SCIENCE OF PRANAYAMA by Swami Sivananda, published by the Divine Life Society, Rishikesh, India.

SERPENT POWER by Arthur Avalon, published by Dover Publications, New York.

SIVANANDA COMPANION TO YOGA (known as BOOK OF YOGA in Britain) by Sivananda Yoga Vedanta Centre, published by Gaia Books, London.

SIVANANDA UPANISHAD, edited by Swami Vishnu-devananda, published by OM Lotus Publishing Company, New York.

SIVA SAMHITA translated by Rai Bahadur Srisa Chandra Vasu, published by Oriental Books Reprint Corporation, New Delhi.

SRIMAD BHAGAVATAM translated by Kamala Subramaniam, published by Bharatiya Vidya Bhavan, Bombay, India

TALKS ON SANKARA'S VIVEKACHOODAMANI with translation and commentary by Swami Chinmayananda, published by Central Chinmaya Mission Trust, Bombay, India

YOGA ASANAS by Swami Sivananda, published by the Divine Life Society, Rishikesh, India.

YOGA MIND & BODY by Sivananda Yoga Vedanta Centre, published by Dorling Kindersley, London.

ASHRAMS

Sivananda Ashram
Yoga Camp
8th Avenue, Val Morin
Quebec JOT 2RO,
CANADA
Tel: (819) 322-3226
Fax: (819) 322-5876
email: HQ@sivananda.org

Sivananda Ashram
Yoga Ranch Colony
P.O. Box 195, Budd Road
Woodbourne, NY 12788
U.S.A
Tel: (914) 434-9242
Fax: (914) 434-1032
email: YogaRanch@sivananda.org

Sivananda Ashram
Yoga Retreat
P.O. Box N7550, Nassau,
BAHAMAS
Tel: (242) 363-2902
Fax: (242) 363-3783
e-mail: YogaRetreat@sivananda.org

Sivananda Yoga Vedanta
Dhanwanthari Ashram
P.O.Neyyar Dam,
Thiruvanthapuram Dt.
Kerala 695 576 INDIA
Tel/Fax: (0471) 290-493
email: YogaIndia@sivananda.org

Sivananda Ashram
Yoga Farm
14651 Ballantree Lane, Comp. 8
Grass Valley, CA 95949
U.S.A.
Tel: (916) 272-9322
Fax: (916) 477-6054
email: YogaFarm@sivananda.org

Sivananda Kutir
(near Siror Bridge)
P.O. Netala, Uttara Kashi Dt
(Himalayas) U.P. 249 193
INDIA
Tel: (01374) 2624

CENTERS

AUSTRIA
Sivananda Yoga Vedanta
Zentrum
Rechte Wienzeile 29-3-9
A-1040 Vienna
Tel: (01) 586-3453
Fax: (01) 587-1551
email: Vienna@sivananda.org

CANADA
Sivananda Yoga
Vedanta Centre
5178 St Lawrence Blvd
Montreal, Quebec H2T 1R8
Tel: (514) 279-3545
Fax: (514) 279-3527
email: Montreal@sivananda.org

Sivananda Yoga
Vedanta Centre
77 Harbord Street
Toronto, Ontario M5S 1G4
Tel: (416) 966-9642
Fax: (416) 966-1378
email: Toronto@sivananda.org

FRANCE
Centre de Yoga
Sivananda Vedanta
123 Boul. Sebastopol
F-75002 Paris
Tel: (01) 40-26-77-49
Fax: (01) 42-33-51-97
email: Paris@sivananda.org

GERMANY
Sivananda Yoga
Vedanta Zentrum
Steinheilstr. 1
D-80333 Munich
Tel: (089) 52-44-76 / 52-17-35
Fax: (089) 52-91-28
email: Munich@sivananda.org

Sivananda Yoga
Vedanta Zentrum
Schmiljanstr. 24
D-12161 Berlin
Tel: (030) 8599 9799
Fax: (030) 8599 9797
email: Berlin@sivananda.org

INDIA
Sivananda Yoga Vedanta
Nataraja Centre
52 Community Centre,
East of Kailash
New Delhi 110 065
Tel: (011) 648-0869
Fax: (011) 645-3962
email: Delhi@sivananda.org

Sivananda Yoga
Vedanta Centre
37/1929, West Fort,
Airport Road
Tiruvananthapuram,
Kerala 695 023
Tel: (0471) 450-942
Fax: (0471) 451-776

Sivananda Yoga
Vedanta Centre
A-9, 7th Main Rd,
Thiruvalluvavar Nagar
Thiruvanmiyur , Chennai
(Madras) 600 0841
Tel: (044) 490-1626
email: Madras@sivananda.org

ISRAEL
Sivananda Yoga
Vedanta Centre
6 Lateris St.,
Tel Aviv 64166
Tel: (03) 691-6793
Fax: (03) 696-3939
email: TelAviv@sivananda.org

Sivananda Yoga
Vedanta Centre
Haportzim St. No. 17,
Petach Tikva 49630
Tel: (03) 924-3841
Fax: (03) 938-3305

SPAIN
Centro de Yoga
Sivananda Vedanta
Calle Eraso 4
E-28028 Madrid
Tel: (01) 361-5150
Fax: (01) 361-5194
email: Madrid@sivananda.org

SWITZERLAND
Centre de Yoga
Sivananda Vedanta
1 Rue de Minoteries
CH-1205 Geneva
Tel: (022) 328-0328
Fax: (022) 320-6117
email: Geneva@sivananda.org

URUGUAY
Asociacion de
Yoga Sivananda
Acevedo Diaz 1523
11200 Montevideo
Tel: (02) 41-09-29 / 41-66-85
Fax: (02) 40-73-88
email:
Montevideo@sivananda.org

UNITED KINGDOM
Sivananda Yoga
Vedanta Centre
51 Felsham Road
London SW15 1AZ
Tel: (0181) 780-0160
Fax: (0181) 780-0128
email: siva@dial.pipex.com

UNITED STATES
Sivananda Yoga
Vedanta Center
243 West 24th Street
New York, NY 10011
Tel: (212) 255-4560
Fax: (212) 727-7392
email: NewYork@sivananda.org

Sivananda Yoga
Vedanta Center
1200 Arguella Blvd
San Francisco, CA 94122
Tel: (415) 681-2731
Fax: (415) 681-5162
email:
SanFrancisco@sivananda.org

Sivananda Yoga
Vedanta Center
1246 Bryn Mawr, Chicago,
IL 60660
Tel: (312) 878-7771
Fax: (312) 878-7527
email: Chicago@sivananda.org

SivanandaYoga
Vedanta Centre
1813 "K"St. - 2nd Floor
Sacramento, CA 95814
Tel: (916) 442-0337
e-mail:
Sacramento@sivananda.org

Sivananda Yoga
Vedanta Center
1746 Abbot Kinney Blvd
Venice (Los Angeles),
CA 90291
Tel: (310) 822-9642
Fax: (310) 301-4214
email:
LosAngeles@sivananda.org